**REGENTS PREPARATION, LLC.**

-Presents-

ALGEBRA II

REGENTS EXAM
REVIEW MANUAL

WITH 8 REGENTS EXAMS,
6 TOPICALLY ORGANIZED

Production

Printed in the United States of America
ISBN: 978-0-578-19769-2

Algebra II
Table of Contents

Polynomial Expressions and Equations

1. Evaluate $j(-1)$ given
$j(x) = 2x^4 - x^3 - 35x^2 + 16x + 48$. ◯
Explain what your answer tells you about
$x + 1$ as a factor.   it is a facto

   08 2018 34

   Algebraically find the remaining zeros of $f(x)$.

2. Over the set of integers, factor the expression   08 2018 25

   $$x^4 - 4x^2 - 12.$$

3. Which expression is equivalent to   08 2018 14
$x^6 y^4 (x^4 - 16) - 9(x^4 - 16)$?

   1) $x^{10} y^4 - 16x^6 y^4 - 9x^4 - 144$

   2) $(x^6 y^4 - 9)(x + 2)^3 (x - 2)$

   3) $(x^3 y^2 + 3)(x^3 y^2 - 3)(x + 2)^2 (x - 2)^2$

   4) $(x^3 y^2 + 3)(x^3 y^2 - 3)(x^2 + 4)(x^2 - 4)$

   X Y ^{104}

Polynomial Expressions and Equations

4. The roots of the equation $3x^2 + 2x = -7$ are

08 2018 09

1) $-2, -\dfrac{1}{3}$

3) $-\dfrac{1}{3} \pm \dfrac{2i\sqrt{5}}{3}$

2) $-\dfrac{7}{3}, 1$

4) $-\dfrac{1}{3} \pm \dfrac{\sqrt{11}}{3}$

5. Which expression is equivalent to

08 2018 05

$$\frac{2x^4 + 8x^3 - 25x^2 - 6x + 14}{x + 6}?$$

1) $2x^3 + 4x^2 + x - 12 + \dfrac{86}{x + 6}$

2) $2x^3 - 4x^2 - x + 14$

3) $2x^3 - 4x^2 - x + \dfrac{14}{x + 6}$

4) $2x^3 - 4x^2 - x$

6.　Consider the function $p(x) = 3x^3 + x^2 - 5x$ and the graph of $y = m(x)$ below.

08 2018 04

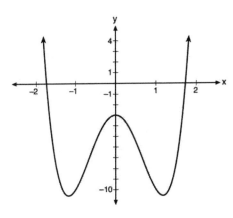

Which statement is true?

1) $p(x)$ has three real roots and $m(x)$ has two real roots.

3)　$p(x)$ has two real roots and $m(x)$ has three real roots.

2) $p(x)$ has one real root and $m(x)$ has two real roots.

4)　$p(x)$ has three real roots and $m(x)$ has four real roots.

7.　If $f(x) = x^2 + 9$ and $g(x) = x + 3$, which operation would not result in a polynomial expression?

08 2018 03

1) $f(x) + g(x)$

3) $f(x) \cdot g(x)$

2) $f(x) - g(x)$

4) $f(x) \div g(x)$

8. Determine the quotient and remainder When $(6a^3 + 11a^2 - 4a - 9)$ is divided by $(3a - 2)$.

   06 2018 29

   Express your answer in the form $q(a) + \dfrac{r(a)}{d(a)}$.

9. Given the following polynomials

   06 2018 22

   $$x = (a + b + c)^2$$
   $$y = a^2 + b^2 + c^2$$
   $$z = ab + bc + ac$$

   Which identity is true?

   1) $x = y - z$ 3) $x = y - 2z$

   2) $x = y + z$ 4) $x = y + 2z$

10. Which equation represents a parabola with a focus of $(-2, 5)$ and a directrix of $y = 9$?

    06 2018 21

    1) $(y - 7)^2 = 8(x + 2)$ 3) $(x + 2)^2 = 8(y - 7)$

    2) $(y - 7)^2 = -8(x + 2)$ 4) $(x + 2)^2 = -8(y - 7)$

    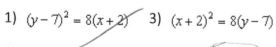

4

11. The profit function, $p(x)$, for a company is the cost function, $c(x)$, subtracted from the revenue function, $r(x)$. The profit function for the Acme Corporation is $p(x) = -0.5x^2 + 250x - 300$ and the revenue function is $r(x) = -0.3x^2 + 150x$.

06 2018 13

The cost function for the Acme Corporation is

1) $c(x) = 0.2x^2 - 100x + 300$ 3) $c(x) = -0.2x^2 + 100x - 300$

2) $c(x) = 0.2x^2 + 100x + 300$ 4) $c(x) = -0.8x^2 + 400x - 300$

12. If $x - 1$ is a factor of $x^3 - kx^2 + 2x$, what is the value of k?

06 2018 12

1) 0   3) 3

2) 2   4) -3

13. Which expression can be rewritten as $(x + 7)(x - 1)$?

06 2018 08

1) $(x + 3)^2 - 16$

2) $(x + 3)^2 - 10(x + 3) - 2(x + 3) + 20$

3) $\dfrac{(x - 1)(x^2 - 6x - 7)}{(x + 1)}$

4) $\dfrac{(x + 7)(x^2 + 4x + 3)}{(x + 3)}$

   5

14. The graphs of the equations $y = x^2 + 4x - 1$ and $y + 3 = x$ are drawn on the same set of axes. One solution of this system is

06 2018 01

1) $(-5, -2)$ 3) $(1, 4)$

2) $(-1, -4)$ 4) $(-2, -1)$

15. On a set of axes, sketch a possible Function $p(x) = (x - a)(x - b)(x + c)$, where a, b, and c are positive, $a > b$, and $p(x)$ has a positive y-intercept of d. Label all intercepts.

08 2017 32

16. Verify the following Pythagorean identity for all values of x and y:

$$(x^2 + y^2)^2 = (x^2 - y^2)^2 + (2xy)^2$$

08 2017 27

17. Which binomial is *not* a factor of the expression $x^3 - 11x^2 + 16x + 84$?

08 2017 20

1) $x + 2$ 3) $x - 6$

2) $x + 4$ 4) $x - 7$

Polynomial Expressions and Equations

18. Which expression has been rewritten correctly to form a true statement?

08 2017 15

1) $(x + 2)^2 + 2(x + 2) - 8 = (x + 6)x$

2) $x^4 + 4x^2 + 9x^2y^2 - 36y^2 = (x + 3y)^2(x - 2)^2$

3) $x^3 + 3x^2 - 4xy^2 - 12y^2 = (x - 2y)(x + 3)^2$

4) $(x^2 - 4)^2 - 5(x^2 - 4) - 6 = (x^2 - 7)(x^2 - 6)$

19. Which expression is equivalent to $\dfrac{4x^3 + 9x - 5}{2x - 1}$, where $x \neq \dfrac{1}{2}$?

08 2017 13

1) $2x^2 + x + 5$ 3) $2x^2 - x + 5$

2) $2x^2 + \dfrac{11}{2} + \dfrac{1}{2(2x - 1)}$ 4) $2x^2 - x + 4 + \dfrac{1}{2x - 1}$

20. A polynomial equation of degree three, $p(x)$, is used to model the volume of a rectangular box. The graph of $p(x)$ has x intercepts at -2, 10, and 14. Which statements regarding $p(x)$ could be true?

08 2017 12

A. The equation of $p(x) = (x - 2)(x + 10)(x + 14)$.

B. The equation of $p(x) = -(x + 2)(x - 10)(x - 14)$.

C. The maximum volume occurs when $x = 10$.

D. The maximum volume of the box is approximately 56.

1) A and C 3) B and C

2) A and D 4) B and D

21. What are the zeros of $P(m) = (m^2 - 4)(m^2 + 1)$?   08 2017 08

     1) 2 and -2, only   3) $-4, i,$ and $-i$

     2) $2, -2,$ and -4 4) $2, -2, i,$ and $-i$

22. Which equation represents a parabola with the focus at $(0, -1)$ and the directrix of $y = 1$?   08 2017 06

     1) $x^2 = -8y$ 3) $x^2 = 8y$

     2) $x^2 = -4y$ 4) $x^2 = 4y$

23. Over the set of integers, factor the expression $4x^3 - x^2 + 16x - 4$ completely.   06 2017 27

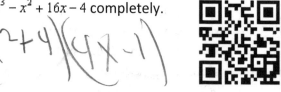

$(x^2 + 4)(4x - 1)$

24. Given $r(x) = x^3 - 4x^2 + 4x - 6$, find the value of $r(2)$. What does your answer tell you about $x - 2$ as a factor of $r(x)$? Explain.   06 2017 25

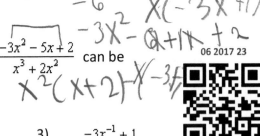

25. The expression $\dfrac{-3x^2 - 5x + 2}{x^3 + 2x^2}$ can be

rewritten as

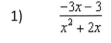

1) $\dfrac{-3x - 3}{x^2 + 2x}$ 3) $-3x^{-1} + 1$

2) $\dfrac{-3x - 1}{x^2}$ 4) $-3x^{-1} + x^{-2}$

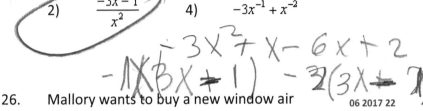

26. Mallory wants to buy a new window air
conditioning unit. The cost for the unit is
$329.99. If she plans to run the unit three
months out of the year for an annual
operating cost of $108.78, which function
models the cost per year over the lifetime
of the unit, $C(n)$, in terms of the number
of years, n, that she owns the air conditioner.

1) $C(n) = 329.99 + 108.78n$

2) $C(n) = 329.99 + 326.34n$

3) $C(n) = \dfrac{329.99 + 108.78n}{n}$

4) $C(n) = \dfrac{329.99 + 326.34n}{n}$

27. A parabola has its focus at $(1, 2)$ and its directrix is $y = -2$. The equation of this parabola could be

06 2017 17

1) $y = 8(x + 1)^2$

2) $y = \dfrac{1}{8}(x + 1)^2$

3) $y = 8(x - 1)^2$

4) $y = \dfrac{1}{8}(x - 1)^2$

28. Which binomial is a factor of
$x^4 - 4x^2 - 4x + 8$?

06 2017 11

1) $x - 2$ 3) $x - 4$

2) $x + 2$ 4) $x + 4$

29. A manufacturing company has developed a cost model, $C(x) = 0.15x^3 + 0.01x^2 + 2x + 120$, where x is the number of items sold, in thousands. The sales price can be modeled by $S(x) = 30 - 0.01x$. Therefore, revenue is modeled by $R(x) = x \bullet S(x)$. The company's profit, $P(x) = R(x) - C(x)$, could be modeled by

06 2017 09

1) $0.15x^3 + 0.02x^2 - 28x + 120$

2) $-0.15x^3 - 0.02x^2 + 28x - 120$

3) $-0.15x^3 + 0.01x^2 - 2.01x - 120$

4) $-0.15x^3 + 32x + 120$

30. Which factorization is *incorrect*? 08 2016 05

1) $4k^2 - 49 = (2k + 7)(2k - 7)$

2) $a^3 - 8b^3 = (a - 2b)(a^2 + 2ab + 4b^2)$

3) $m^3 + 3m^2 - 4m + 12 = (m - 2)^2(m + 3)$

4) $t^3 + 5t^2 + 6t + t^2 + 5t + 6 = (t + 1)(t + 2)(t + 3)$

31. The expression $\dfrac{x^3 + 2x^2 + x + 6}{x + 2}$ is equivalent 08 2016 11 to

1) $x^2 + 3$ 3) $2x^2 + x + 6$

2) $x^2 + 1 + \dfrac{4}{x + 2}$ 4) $2x^2 + 1 + \dfrac{4}{x + 2}$

32. The completely factored form of $2d^4 + 6d^3 - 18d^2 - 54d$ is 08 2016 15

1) $2d(d^2 - 9)(d + 3)$

2) $2d(d^2 + 9)(d + 3)$

3) $2d(d + 3)^2(d - 3)$

4) $2d(d - 3)^2(d + 3)$

33. Mr. Farison gave his class the three mathematical rules shown below to either prove or disprove. Which rules can be proved for all real numbers?

08 2016 20

I $(m+p)^2 = m^2 + 2mp + p^2$

II $(x+y)^3 = x^3 + 3xy + y^3$

III $(a^2+b^2)^2 = (a^2-b^2)^2 + (2ab)^2$

1)	I, only	3)	II and III
2)	I and II	4)	I and III

34. The graph of $p(x)$ is shown below.

08 2016 21

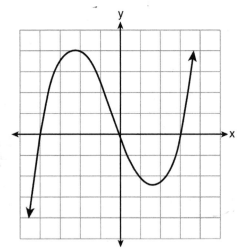

What is the remainder when $p(x)$ is divided by $x+4$?

1)	$x-4$	3)	0
2)	-4	4)	4

35. Find algebraically the zeros for

08 2016 33

$p(x) = x^3 + x^2 - 4x - 4$.

On the set of axes below, graph $y = p(x)$.

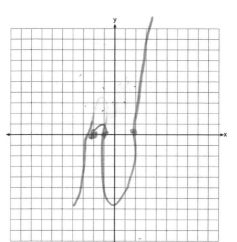

36. The zeros for $f(x) = x^4 - 4x^3 - 9x^2 + 36x$ are

06 2016 06

1) $\{0, \pm 3, 4\}$ 3) $\{0, \pm 3, -4\}$

2) $\{0, 3, 4\}$ 4) $\{0, 3, -4\}$

37. A solution of the equation $2x^2 + 3x + 2 = 0$ is

06 2016 12

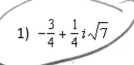

1) $-\dfrac{3}{4} + \dfrac{1}{4}i\sqrt{7}$ 3) $-\dfrac{3}{4} + \dfrac{1}{4}\sqrt{7}$

2) $-\dfrac{3}{4} + \dfrac{1}{4}i$ 4) $\dfrac{1}{2}$

38. Which value, to the *nearest tenth*, is *not* a solution of $p(x) = q(x)$ if $p(x) = x^3 + 3x^2 - 3x - 1$ and $q(x) = 3x + 8$?

06 2016 22

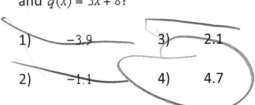

1) −3.9   3) 2.1

2) −1.1   4) 4.7

39. Determine if $x - 5$ is a factor of $2x^3 - 4x^2 - 7x - 10$. Explain your answer.

06 2016 27

X-5 is not a factor the remainder is 5

40. The directrix of the parabola $12(y + 3) = (x - 4)^2$ has the equation $y = -6$.

06 2016 30

P = 3

Find the coordinates of the focus of the parabola.

F(4, 0)

41. Which function shown below has a greater average rate of change on the interval $[-2, 4]$ Justify your answer.

06 2016 36

x	f(x)
−4	0.3125
−3	0.625
−2	1.25
−1	2.5
0	5
1	10
2	20
3	40
4	80
5	160
6	320

[handwritten student work:] $g(x)$ has a higher

$-2-$
-2

$4 , 38$

0.0

$-2, 1.25$

3.125 .25 −

Complex Numbers

1. Given $c(m) = m^3 - 2m^2 + 4m - 8$, the solution of $c(m) = 0$ is

    08 2018 21

    1) ± 2

    3) $2i, 2$

    2) 2, only

    4) $\pm 2i, 2$

2. If $A = -3 + 5i$, $B = 4 - 2i$, and $C = 1 + 6i$, where i is the imaginary unit, then $A - BC$ equals

    08 2018 15

    1) $5 - 17i$

    3) $-19 - 17i$

    2) $5 + 27i$

    4) $-19 + 27i$

3. Solve the equation $2x^2 + 5x + 8 = 0.$ Express the answer in $a + bi$ form.

    06 2018 27

4. Where i is the imaginary unit, the expression $(x + 3i)^2 - (2x - 3i)^2$ is equivalent to

    06 2018 05

    1) $-3x^2$

    3) $-3x^2 - 18xi$

    2) $-3x^2 - 18$

    4) $-3x^2 - 6xi - 18$

5. The roots of the equation $x^2 + 2x + 5 = 0$ are

08 2017 03

1) -3 and 1

3) $-1 + 2i$ and $-1 - 2i$

2) -1, only

4) $-1 + 4i$ and $-1 - 4i$

6. Which expression is equivalent to $(3k - 2i)^2$, where i is the imaginary unit?

08 2017 02

1) $9k^2 - 4$

3) $9k^2 - 12ki - 4$

2) $9k^2 + 4$

4) $9k^2 - 12ki + 4$

7. The solution to the equation $4x^2 + 98 = 0$ is

06 2017 07

1) ± 7

3) $\pm \dfrac{7\sqrt{2}}{2}$

2) $\pm 7i$

4) $\pm \dfrac{7i\sqrt{2}}{2}$

8. The expression $6xi^3(-4xi + 5)$ is equivalent to

06 2017 04

1) $2x - 5i$

3) $-24x^2 + 30x - i$

2) $-24x^2 - 30xi$

4) $26x - 24x^2i - 5i$

Complex Numbers

9.   Which equation has $1-i$ as a solution?

08 2016 01

    1) $x^2 + 2x - 2 = 0$

    2) $x^2 + 2x + 2 = 0$

    3) $x^2 - 2x - 2 = 0$

    4) $x^2 - 2x + 2 = 0$

10.   Simplify $xi(i - 7i)^2$, where i is the Imaginary unit.

08 2016 27

11.   Given i is the imaginary unit, $(2 - yi)^2$ in simplest form is

06 2016 03

    1) $y^2 - 4yi + 4$

    2) $-y^2 - 4yi + 4$

    3) $-y^2 + 4$

    4) $y^2 + 4$

Exponential Expressions and Equations

1. Determine, to the *nearest tenth of a year,* kow long it would take an investment to double at a $3\frac{3}{4}\%$ interest rate, compounded continuously.

08 2018 35

$A = pe^{rt}$

$2 = e^{.0375t}$ $\ln 2 = .0375t$

2. The world population was 2560 million people in 1950 and 3040 million in 1960 and can be modeled by the function $p(t) = 2560e^{0.017185t}$, where t is time in years after 1950 and $p(t)$ is the population in millions. Determine the average rate of change of $p(t)$ in millions of people per year, from $4 \leq t \leq 8$.

08 2018 27

Round your answer to the *nearest hundredth*.

3. Express the fraction $\dfrac{2x^{\frac{3}{2}}}{\left(16x^{1}\right)^{\frac{1}{4}}}$ in simplest radical form.

08 2018 26

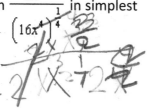

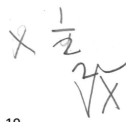

Exponential Expressions and Equations

4. Jake wants to buy a car and hopes to save at least $5000 for a down payment. The table below summarizes the amount of money he plans to save each week.

08 2018 13

Week	1	2	3	4	5
Money Saved, in Dollars	2	5	12.5	31.25	...

Based on this plan, which expression should he use to determine how much he has saved in *n* weeks?

1) $\dfrac{2-2(2.5^x)}{1-2.5}$

3) $\dfrac{1-2.5^x}{1-2.5}$

2) $\dfrac{2-2(2.5^{x-1})}{1-2.5}$

4) $\dfrac{1-2.5^{x-1}}{1-2.5}$

5. The average depreciation rate of a new boat is approximately 8% per year. If a new boat is purchased at a price of $75,000, which model is a recursive formula representing the value of the boat *n* years after it was purchased?

08 2018 10

1) $a_x = 75,000(0.08)^x$

3) $a_x = 75,000(1.08)^x$

2) $a_0 = 75,000$
   $a_x = (0.92)^x$

4) $a_0 = 75,000$
   $a_x = 0.92(a_{x-1})$

6. Stephanie found that the number of white-winged cross bills in an area can be represented by the formula $C = 550(1.08)^t$, where t represents the number of years since 2010. Which equation correctly represents the number of white-winged cross bills in terms of the monthly rate of population growth?

08 2018 08

1) $C = 550(1.00643)^t$ 3) $C = 550(1.00643)^{\frac{t}{12}}$

2) $C = 550(1.00643)^{12t}$ 4) $C = 550(1.00643)^{t+12}$

7. The solution of $87e^{0.3x} = 5918$, to the *nearest thousandth*, is

08 2018 01

1) 0.583   3) 4.220

2) 1.945   4) 14.066

8. Carla wants to start a college fund for her daughter Lila. She puts $63,000 into an account that grows at a rate of 2.55% per year, compounded monthly. function, $C(t)$, that represents the amount of money in the account t years after the account is opened, given that no more money is deposited into or withdrawn from the account. Calculate algebraically the number of years it will take for the account to reach $100,000, to the *nearest hundredth of a year.*

06 2018 35

$$1000 = 63,000\left(1 - .0155\right)^t$$

21

9. The Wells family is looking to purchase a home in a suburb of Rochester with a 30-year mortgage that has an annual interest rate of 3.6%. The house the family wants to purchase is $152,500 and they will make a $15,250 down payment and borrow the remainder. Use the formula below to determine their monthly payment, to the *nearest dollar*.

06 2018 31

$$M = \frac{P\left(\dfrac{r}{12}\right)\left(1 + \dfrac{r}{12}\right)^{n}}{\left(1 + \dfrac{r}{12}\right)^{n} - 1}$$

M = monthly payment
P = amount borrowed
r = annual interest rate
n = total number of monthly payments

10. On average, college seniors graduating in 2012 could compute their growing student loan debt using the function
$$D(t) = 29,400(1.068)^{t},$$
where t is time in years. Which expression is equivalent to $29,400(1.068)^{t}$ and could be used by students to identify an approximate daily interest rate on their loans?

06 2018 23

Exponential Expressions and Equations

1) $$29,400\left(1.068^{\frac{1}{365}}\right)^{t}$$

3) $$29,400\left(1+\frac{0.068}{365}\right)^{t}$$

2) $$29,400\left(\frac{1.068}{365}\right)^{365t}$$

4) $$29,400\left(1.068^{\frac{1}{365}}\right)^{365t}$$

11. The graph of $y = \log_2 x$ is translated to the right 1 unit and down 1 unit.
The coordinates of the x-intercept of the translated graph are

06 2018 19

1) $(0,0)$

3) $(2,0)$

2) $(1,0)$

4) $(3,0)$

12. The half-life of iodine-131 is 8 days.
The percent of the isotope left in the body d days after being introduced is

06 2018 18

$I = 100\left(\frac{1}{2}\right)^{\frac{d}{8}}$. When this equation is

written in terms of the number e, the base of the natural logarithm, it is equivalent to $I = 100e^{kd}$. What is the approximate value of the constant, k?

1) -0.087

3) -11.542

2) 0.087

4) 11.542

13. The populations of two small towns at the beginning of 2018 and their annual population growth rate are shown in the table below.

06 2018 14

Town	Population	Annual Population Growth Rate
Jonesville	1240	6% increase
Williamstown	890	11% increase

Assuming the trend continues, approximately how many years after the beginning of 2018 will it take for the populations to be equal?

1) 7

3) 68

2) 20

4) 125

14. The function $N(t) = 100e^{-0.023t}$ models the number of grams in a sample of cesium-137 that remain after t years. On which interval is the sample's average rate of decay the fastest?

06 2018 07

1) [1, 10]

3) [15, 25]

2) [10, 20]

4) [1, 30]

15. A scatterplot showing the weight, *w*, in grams, of each crystal after growing *t* hours is shown below.

06 2018 04

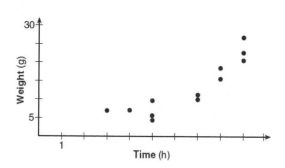

The relationship between weight, *w*, and time, *t*, is best modeled by

1) $w = 4^t + 5$

3) $w = 5(2.1)^t$

2) $w = (1.4)^t + 2$

4) $w = 8(.75)^t$

16. Which statement is true about the graph of

$$f(x) = \left(\frac{1}{8}\right)^x ?$$

06 2018 02

1) The graph is always increasing.
2) The graph is always decreasing.
3) The graph passes through $(1, 0)$.
4) The graph has an asymptote, $x = 0$.

Exponential Expressions and Equations

17. The value of a certain small passenger car based on its use in years is modeled by $V(t) = 28482.698(0.684)^t$ where $V(t)$ is the value in dollars and t is the time in years. Zach had to take out a loan to purchase the small passenger car. The function $Z(t) = 22151.327(0.778)^t$, where $Z(t)$ is measured in dollars, and t is the time in years, models the unpaid amount of Zach's loan over time. Graph $V(t)$ and $Z(t)$ over the interval $0 \le t \le 5$, on the set of axes below.

08 2017 37

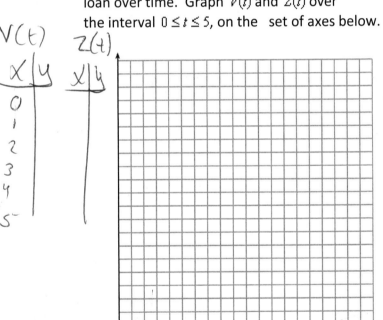

$V(t)$

x	y
0	
1	
2	
3	
4	
5	

$Z(t)$

x	y

State when $V(t) = Z(t)$, to the *nearest hundredth*, and interpret its meaning in the context of the problem. Zach takes out an insurance policy that requires him to pay a $3000 deductible in case of a collision. Zach will cancel the collision policy when the value of his car equals his deductible.

To the *nearest year*, how long will it take Zach to cancel this policy?

Justify your answer.

18. Using a microscope, a researcher observed and recorded the number of bacteria spores on a large sample of uniformly sized pieces of meat kept at room temperature. A summary of the data she recorded is shown in the table below.

08 2017 36

Hours (x)	Average Number of Spores (y)
0	4
0.5	10
1	15
2	60
3	260
4	1130
6	16,380

Exponential Expressions and Equations

Using these data, write an exponential regression equation, rounding all values to the *nearest thousandth*.

The researcher knows that people are likely to suffer from food-borne illness if the number of spores exceeds 100.

Using the exponential regression equation, determine the maximum amount of time, to the *nearest quarter hour*, that the meat can be kept at room temperature safely.

19. In New York State, the minimum wage has grown exponentially. In 1966, the minimum wage was $1.25 an hour and in 2015, it was $8.75. Algebraically determine the rate of growth to the *nearest percent*.

08 2017 30

20. Iridium-192 is an isotope of iridium and has a half- life of 73.83 days. If a laboratory experiment begins with 100 grams of Iridium-192, the number of grams, *A*, of

08 2017 10

Iridium-192 present after *t* days would be

$$A = 100\left(\frac{1}{2}\right)^{\frac{t}{73.83}}.$$

Which equation approximates the amount of Iridium-192 present after *t* days?

1) $A = 100\left(\dfrac{73.83}{2}\right)^t$ 3) $A = 100(0.990656)^t$

2) $A = 100\left(\dfrac{1}{147.66}\right)^t$ 4) $A = 100(0.116381)^t$

21. The value of a new car depreciates over time. Greg purchased a new car in June 2011. The value, V, of his car after t years can be modeled by the equation $\log_{0.8}\left(\dfrac{V}{1700}\right) = t$. What is the average decreasing rate of change per year of the value of the car from June 2012 to June 2014, to the *nearest ten dollars per year*?

08 2017 09

1) 1960   3) 2450

2) 2180   4) 2770

22. A radioactive substance has a mass of 140 g at 3 p.m. and 100 g at 8 p.m. Write an equation in the form $A = A_0\left(\dfrac{1}{2}\right)^{\frac{t}{h}}$ that models this situation, where h is the constant representing the number of hours in the half-life, A_0 is the initial mass, and A is the mass t hours after 3 p.m. Using this equation, solve for h, to the *nearest ten thousandth*. Determine when the mass of the radioactive substance will be 40 g. Round your answer to the *nearest tenth of an hour*.

06 2017 37

Exponential Expressions and Equations

23. Jim is looking to buy a vacation home for $172,600 near his favorite southern beach. The formula to compute a mortgage payment, *M*, is $M = P \cdot \dfrac{r(1+r)^N}{(1+r)^N - 1}$ where

    P is the principal amount of the loan, *r* is the monthly interest rate, and *N* is the number of monthly payments. Jim's bank offers a monthly interest rate of 0.305% for a 15-year mortgage. With no down payment, determine Jim's mortgage payment, rounded to the *nearest dollar*.

    Algebraically determine and state the down payment, rounded to the *nearest dollar*, that Jim needs to make in order for his mortgage payment to be $1100.

24. Write $\sqrt[3]{x} \cdot \sqrt{x}$ as a single term with a rational exponent.

25. Jasmine decides to put $100 in a savings account each month. The account pays 3% annual interest, compounded monthly. How much money, S, will Jasmine have after one year?

06 2017 24

1) $S = 100(1.03)^{12}$

2) $S = \dfrac{100 - 100(1.0025)^{12}}{1 - 1.0025}$

3) $S = 100(1.0025)^{12}$

4) $S = \dfrac{100 - 100(1.03)^{12}}{1 - 1.03}$

26. The function $p(t) = 110e^{0.03922t}$ models the population of a city, in millions, t years after 2010. As of today, consider the following two statements:

06 2017 18

I. The current population is 110 million.

II. The population increases continuously by approximately 3.9% per year.

This model supports

1) I, only
2) II, only
3) both I and II
4) neither I nor II

Exponential Expressions and Equations

27. For $x \neq 0$, which expressions are equivalent to one divided by the sixth root of x?

06 2017 16

I. $\dfrac{\sqrt[6]{x}}{\sqrt[3]{x}}$

II. $\dfrac{x^{\frac{1}{6}}}{x^{\frac{1}{3}}}$

III. $x^{\frac{-1}{6}}$

1) I and II, only

2) I and III, only

3) II and III, only

4) I, II, and III

28. A student studying public policy created a model for the population of Detroit, where the population decreased 25% over a decade. He used the model $P = 714(0.75)^d$, where P is the population, in thousands, d decades after 2010. Another student, Suzanne, wants to use a model that would predict the population after y years. Suzanne's model is best represented by

06 2017 13

1) $P = 714(0.6500)^y$

2) $P = 714(0.8500)^y$

3) $P = 714(0.9716)^y$

4) $P = 714(0.9750)^y$

Exponential Expressions and Equations

29. What is the solution to $8(2^{x+3}) = 48$?

06 2017 02

1) $x = \dfrac{\ln 6}{\ln 2} - 3$ 3) $x = \dfrac{\ln 48}{\ln 16} - 3$

2) $x = 0$ 4) $x = \ln 4 - 3$

30. An equation to represent the value of a car after t months of ownership is

08 2016 13

$$v = 32,000(0.81)^{\frac{t}{12}}.$$

Which statement is *not* correct?

1) The car lost approximately 19% of its value each month.

2) The car maintained approximately 98% of its value each month.

3) The value of the car when it was purchased was $32,000.

4) The value of the car 1 year after it was purchased was $25,920.

31. A payday loan company makes loans Between $100 and $1000 available to customers. Every 14 days, customers are charged 30% interest with compounding. In 2013, Remi took out a $300 payday loan. expression can be used to calculate the amount she would owe, in dollars, after one year if she did not make payments?

08 2016 22

1) $300(.30)^{\frac{14}{365}}$ 3) $300(.30)^{\frac{365}{14}}$

2) $300(1.30)^{\frac{14}{365}}$ 4) $300(1.30)^{\frac{365}{14}}$

32. In 2010, the population of New York State was approximately 19,378,000 with an annual growth rate of 1.5%. Assuming the growth rate is maintained for a large number of years, which equation can be used to predict the population of New York State t years after 2010?

08 2016 24

1) $P_t = 19,378,000(1.5)^t$

2) $P_0 = 19,378,000$
   $P_t = 19,378,000 + 1.015P_{t-1}$

3) $P_t = 19,378,000(1.015)^{t-1}$

4) $P_0 = 19,378,000$
   $P_t = 1.015P_{t-1}$

34

33. One of the medical uses of Iodine–131 (I–131), a radioactive isotope of iodine, is to enhance x-ray images. The half-life of I–131 is approximately 8.02 days. A patient is injected with 20 milligrams of I–131.

08 2016 34

Determine, to the *nearest day*, the amount of time needed before the amount of I–131 in the patient's body is approximately 7 milligrams.

34. Seth's parents gave him $5000 to invest for his 16th birthday. He is considering two investment options. Option A will pay him 4.5% interest compounded annually. Option B will pay him 4.6% compounded quarterly. Write a function of option A and option B that calculates the value of each account after n years. Seth plans to use the money after he graduates from college in 6 years.

08 2016 37

Determine how much more money option B will earn than option A to the nearest cent.

Algebraically determine, to the nearest tenth of a year, how long it would take for option B to double Seth's initial investment

Exponential Expressions and Equations

35. When $b > 0$ and d is a positive integer, the expression $(3b)^{\frac{2}{d}}$ is equivalent to

06 2016 01

1) $\dfrac{1}{\left(\sqrt[d]{3b}\right)^2}$

3) $\dfrac{1}{\sqrt{3b^d}}$

2) $\left(\sqrt{3b}\right)^d$

4) $\left(\sqrt[d]{3b}\right)^2$

36. Which function represents exponential decay?

06 2016 15

1) $y = 2^{0.3t}$

3) $y = \left(\dfrac{1}{2}\right)^{-t}$

2) $y = 1.2^{3t}$

4) $y = 5^{-t}$

37. Last year, the total revenue for Home Style, a national restaurant chain, increased 5.25% over the previous year. If this trend were to continue, which expression could the company's chief financial officer use to approximate their monthly percent increase in revenue? [Let m represent months.]

06 2016 21

1) $(1.0525)^{m}$

3) $(1.00427)^{m}$

2) $(1.0525)^{\frac{12}{m}}$

4) $(1.00427)^{\frac{m}{12}}$

36

38. A house purchased 5 years ago for $100,000 was just sold for $135,000. Assuming exponential growth, approximate the annual growth rate, to the nearest percent.

06 2016 32

39. Alexa earns $33,000 in her first year of teaching and earns a 4% increase in each successive year.

06 2016 34

Write a geometric series formula, S_n, for Alexa's total earnings over n years.

Use this formula to find Alexa's total earnings for her first 15 years of teaching, to the nearest cent.

40. Drugs break down in the human body at different rates and therefore must be prescribed by doctors carefully to prevent complications, such as overdosing. The breakdown of a drug is represented by the function $N(t) = N_0(e)^{-rt}$,

06 2016 37

where $N(t)$ is the amount left in the body, N_0 is the initial dosage, r is the decay rate, and t is time in hours. Patient A, $A(t)$, is given 800 milligrams of a drug with a decay rate of 0.347. Patient B, $B(t)$, is given 400 milligrams of another drug with a decay rate of 0.231.

Exponential Expressions and Equations

Write two functions, $A(t)$ and $B(t)$, to represent the breakdown of the respective drug given to each patient. Graph each function on the set of axes below.

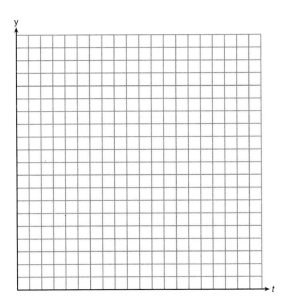

To the nearest hour, t, when does the amount of the given drug remaining in patient B begin to exceed the amount of the given drug remaining in patient A?

The doctor will allow patient A to take another 800 milligram dose of the drug once only 15% of the original dose is left in the body.

Determine, to the nearest tenth of an hour, how long patient A will have to wait to take another 800 milligram dose of the drug.

Rational Expressions and Equations

1. Algebraically solve for x: $\dfrac{-3}{x+3} + \dfrac{1}{2} = \dfrac{x}{6} - \dfrac{1}{2}$

2. A manufacturing plant produces two different-sized containers of peanuts. One container weighs x ounces and the other weighs y pounds. If a gift set can hold one of each size container, which expression represents the number of gift sets needed to hold 124 ounces?

1) $\dfrac{124}{16x+y}$ 3) $\dfrac{124}{x+16y}$

2) $\dfrac{x+16y}{124}$ 4) $\dfrac{16x+y}{124}$

3. What is the solution set of the equation $\dfrac{2}{x} - \dfrac{3x}{x+3} = \dfrac{x}{x+3}$?

1) $\{3\}$ 3) $\{-2,3\}$

2) $\left\{\dfrac{3}{2}\right\}$ 4) $\left\{-1,\dfrac{3}{2}\right\}$

4. Solve for all values of

08 2017 33

p: $\dfrac{3p}{p-5} - \dfrac{2}{p+3} = \dfrac{p}{p+3}$

5. To solve $\dfrac{2x}{x-2} - \dfrac{11}{x} = \dfrac{8}{x^2 - 2x}$, Ren

06 2017 19

multiplied both sides by the least common denominator. Which statement is true?

1) 2 is an extraneous solution.
2) $\dfrac{7}{2}$ is an extraneous solution.
3) 0 and 2 are extraneous solutions.
4) This equation does not contain any extraneous solutions.

6. The focal length, F, of a camera's lens is related to the distance of the object from the lens, J, and the distance to the image area in the camera, W, by the formula below.

08 2016 17

$$\dfrac{1}{J} + \dfrac{1}{W} = \dfrac{1}{F}$$

When this equation is solved for J in terms of F and W, J equals

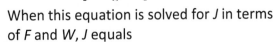

1) $F - W$
3) $\dfrac{FW}{W - F}$

2) $\dfrac{FW}{F - W}$
4) $\dfrac{1}{F} - \dfrac{1}{W}$

7. The expression $\dfrac{4x^3 + 5x + 10}{2x + 3}$ is equivalent to

06 2016 14

1) $2x^2 + 3x - 7 + \dfrac{31}{2x + 3}$

2) $2x^2 - 3x + 7 - \dfrac{11}{2x + 3}$

3) $2x^2 + 2.5x + 5 + \dfrac{15}{2x + 3}$

4) $2x^2 - 2.5x - 5 - \dfrac{20}{2x + 3}$

06 2016 25

8. Solve for x: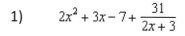

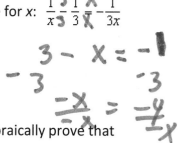

9. Algebraically prove that

06 2016 31

$$\frac{x^3 + 9}{x^3 + 8} = 1 + \frac{1}{x^3 + 8}, \quad \text{where } x \neq -2.$$

Radical Expressions and Equations

1. For $x > 0$, which expression is equivalent to

08 2018 12

$$\frac{\sqrt[3]{x^2} \cdot \sqrt{x^5}}{\sqrt[6]{x}}?$$

1) x 3) x^3

2) $x^{\frac{3}{2}}$ 4) x^{10}

2. The value(s) of x that satisfy

08 2018 07

$$\sqrt{x^2 - 4x - 5} = 2x - 10 \quad \text{are}$$

1) $\{5\}$ 3) $\{5,7\}$

2) $\{7\}$ 4) $\{3,5,7\}$

06 2018 33

3. Solve algebraically for all values of x:

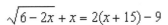

$$\sqrt{6 - 2x} + x = 2(x + 15) - 9$$

4. For positive values of x, which expression

   Is equivalent to $\sqrt{16x^2} \cdot x^{\frac{2}{3}} + \sqrt[3]{8x^5}$

   06 2018 20

   1) $6\sqrt[3]{x^5}$

   2) $6\sqrt[5]{x^3}$

   3) $4\sqrt[3]{x^2} + 2\sqrt[3]{x^5}$

   4) $4\sqrt{x^3} + 2\sqrt[5]{x^3}$

5. For all values of x for which the expression

   is defined, $\dfrac{x^3 + 2x^2 - 9x - 18}{x^3 - x^2 - 6x}$, in simplest

   form, is equivalent to

   06 2018 03

   1) 3

   2) $-\dfrac{17}{2}$

   3) $\dfrac{x+3}{x}$

   4) $\dfrac{x^2 - 9}{x(x-3)}$

6. Explain how $(-8)^{\frac{4}{3}}$ can be evaluated
   using properties of rational exponents
   to result in an integer answer.

   08 2017 25

7. What does $\left(\dfrac{-54x^9}{y^4}\right)^{\frac{2}{3}}$ equal?

08 2017 23

1) $\dfrac{9ix^6\sqrt[3]{4}}{y\sqrt[3]{y^2}}$

3) $\dfrac{9x^6\sqrt[3]{4}}{y\sqrt[3]{y}}$

2) $\dfrac{9ix^6\sqrt[3]{4}}{y^2\sqrt[3]{y^2}}$

4) $\dfrac{9x^6\sqrt[3]{4}}{y^2\sqrt[3]{y^2}}$

8. The solution set for the equation

08 2017 04

$\sqrt{x+14} - \sqrt{2x+5} = 1$ is

1) $\{-6\}$

3) $\{18\}$

2) $\{2\}$

4) $\{2, 22\}$

9. Solve algebraically for all values of x:
    $\sqrt{x-4} + x = 6$

06 2017 30

10. Explain how $\left(3^{\frac{1}{5}}\right)^2$ can be written as the equivalent radical expression $\sqrt[5]{9}$.

08 2016 26

11. Solve the equation $\sqrt{2x-7} + x = 5$ algebraically, and justify the solution set.

08 2016 35

12. The solution set for the equation $\sqrt{56-x} = x$ is

06 2016 05

1) $\{-8, 7\}$ 3) $\{7\}$

2) $\{-7, 8\}$ 4) $\{\ \}$

Trigonometric Expressions and Equations

1. The height above ground for a person riding a Ferris wheel after t seconds is modeled by $h(t) = 150 \sin\left(\dfrac{\pi}{45} t + 67.5\right) + 160$ feet. How many seconds does it take to go from the bottom of the wheel to the top of the wheel?

    08 2018 22

    1) 10   3) 90

    2) 45   4) 150

2. Given $\cos \theta = \dfrac{7}{25}$, where θ is an angle in standard position terminating in quadrant IV, and $\sin^2 \theta + \cos^2 \theta = 1$, what is the value of $\tan \theta$?

    08 2018 11

    1) $-\dfrac{24}{25}$ 3) $\dfrac{24}{25}$

    2) $-\dfrac{24}{7}$ 4) $\dfrac{24}{7}$

3. The height, $h(t)$ in cm, of a piston, is given

06 2018 36

by the equation $h(t) = 12\cos\left(\dfrac{\pi}{3}t\right) + 8$,

where t represents the number of seconds since the measurements began.

Determine the average rate of change, in cm/sec, of the piston's height on the interval $1 \le t \le 2$. At what value(s) of t, to the *nearest tenth of a second*, does $h(t) = 0$ in the interval $1 \le t \le 5$?

Justify your answer.

4. An angle, θ, is in standard position and its terminal side passes through the point $(2, -1)$. Find the *exact* value of $\sin \theta$.

06 2018 32

5. The depth of the water at a marker 20 feet from the shore in a bay is depicted in the graph below.

06 2018 10

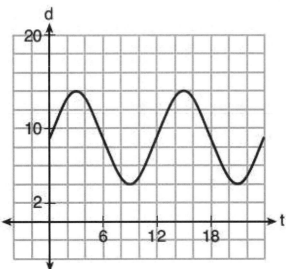

If the depth, *d*, is measured in feet and time, *t*, is measured in hours since midnight, what is an equation for the depth of the water at the marker?

1) $d = 5\cos\left(\dfrac{\pi}{6}t\right) + 9$

2) $d = 9\cos\left(\dfrac{\pi}{6}t\right) + 5$

3) $d = 9\sin\left(\dfrac{\pi}{6}t\right) + 5$

4) $d = 5\sin\left(\dfrac{\pi}{6}t\right) + 9$

6. a) On a set of axes, sketch *at least one* cycle of a sine curve with an amplitude of 2, a midline at $y = -\frac{3}{2}$, and a period of 2π.

08 2017 35

b) Explain any differences between a sketch of $y = 2\sin\left(x - \frac{\pi}{3}\right) - \frac{3}{2}$ and the sketch from part a.

7. Which sinusoid has the greatest amplitude?

08 2017 18

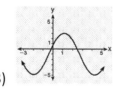

1)

2) $y = 3\sin(\theta - 3) + 5$

3)

4) $y = -5\sin(\theta - 1) - 3$

8. Which diagram represents an angle, α, Measuring $\frac{13\pi}{20}$ radians drawn in standard position, and its reference angle, θ?

08 2017 07

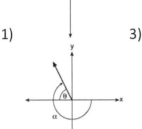

1)   3)

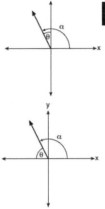

2)   4)

9. As x increases from 0 to $\frac{\pi}{2}$, the graph of the equation $y = 2\tan x$ will

08 2017 05

1) increase from 0 to 2

2) decrease from 0 to -2

3) increase without limit

4) decrease without limit

10. The graph below represents the height above the ground, *h*, in inches, of a point on a tri-athlete's bike wheel during a training ride in terms of time, *t*, in seconds.

06 2017 28

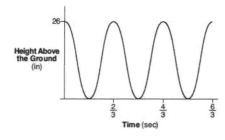

Identify the period of the graph and describe what the period represents in this context.

11. Based on climate data that have been collected in Bar Harbor, Maine, the average monthly temperature, in degrees F, can be modeled by the equation
$B(x) = 23.914 \sin(0.508x - 2.116) + 55.300$.
The same governmental agency collected average monthly temperature data for Phoenix, Arizona, and found the temperatures could be modeled by the equation
$P(x) = 20.238 \sin(0.525x - 2.148) + 86.729$.

06 2017 15

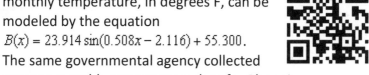

Which statement can *not* be concluded based on the average monthly temperature models *x* months after starting data collection?

1) The average monthly temperature variation is more in Bar Harbor than in Phoenix.

2) The midline average monthly temperature for Bar Harbor is lower than the midline temperature for Phoenix.

3) The maximum average monthly temperature for Bar Harbor is 79° F, to the nearest degree.

4) The minimum average monthly temperature for Phoenix is 20° F, to the nearest degree.

12. Given that $\sin^2\theta + \cos^2\theta = 1$ and $\sin\theta = -\dfrac{\sqrt{2}}{5}$, what is a possible value of $\cos\theta$?

06 2017 12

1) $\dfrac{5+\sqrt{2}}{5}$

2) $\dfrac{\sqrt{23}}{5}$

3) $\dfrac{3\sqrt{3}}{5}$

4) $\dfrac{\sqrt{35}}{5}$

13. Which equation is represented by the graph shown below? 06 2017 08

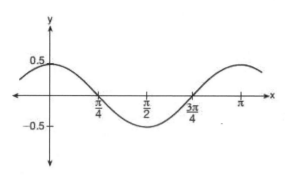

1) $y = \frac{1}{2}\cos 2x$ 2) $y = \cos x$

3) $y = \frac{1}{2}\cos x$ 4) $y = 2\cos \frac{1}{2}x$

14. Given the parent function $p(x) = \cos x$, which phrase best describes the transformation used to obtain the graph of 06 2017 06

$$g(x) = \cos(x+a) - b,$$

if a and b are positive constants?

1) right a units, up b units

2) right a units, down b units

3) left a units, up b units

4) left a units, down b units

15. A sine function increasing through the origin can be used to model light waves. Violet light has a wavelength of 400 nanometers. Over which interval is the height of the wave *decreasing*, only?

08 2016 10

1) $(0, 200)$ 3) $(200, 400)$

2) $(100, 300)$ 4) $(300, 400)$

16. Which diagram shows an angle rotation of 1 radian on the unit circle?

08 2016 16

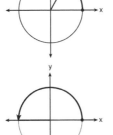

1)

2)

3)

4)

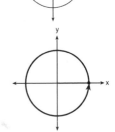

17. The volume of air in a person's lungs, as the person breathes in and out, can be modeled by a sine graph. A scientist is studying the differences in this volume for people at rest compared to people told to take a deep breath. When examining the graphs, should the scientist focus on the amplitude, period, or midline? Explain your choice.

08 2016 25

18. Using the identity $\sin^2\theta + \cos^2\theta = 1$, find the value of $\tan\theta$, to the *nearest hundredth*, if $\cos\theta$ is −0.7 and θ is in Quadrant II.

08 2016 28

19. The Ferris wheel at the landmark Navy Pier in Chicago takes 7 minutes to make one full rotation. The height, H, in feet, above the ground of one of the six-person cars can be modeled by $H(t) = 70\sin\left(\frac{2\pi}{7}(t - 1.75)\right) + 80$, where t is time, in minutes. Using $H(t)$ for one full rotation, this car's minimum height, in feet, is

06 2016 13

1) 150　　　　3) 10

2) 70　　　　4) 0

20. A circle centered at the origin has a radius of 10 units. The terminal side of an angle, θ, intercepts the circle in Quadrant II at point C. The y-coordinate of point C is 8. What is the value of $\cos \theta$?

06 2016 17

1) $-\dfrac{3}{5}$

2) $-\dfrac{3}{4}$

3) $\dfrac{3}{5}$

4) $\dfrac{4}{5}$

21. The voltage used by most households can be modeled by a sine function. The maximum voltage is 120 volts, and there are 60 cycles *every second*. Which equation best represents the value of the voltage as it flows through the electric wires, where t is time in seconds?

06 2016 24

1) $V = 120\sin(t)$

3) $V = 120\sin(60\pi t)$

2) $V = 120\sin(60t)$

4) $V = 120\sin(120\pi t)$

22. On a set of axes, graph *one* cycle of a cosine function with amplitude 3, period $\dfrac{\pi}{2}$, midline $y = -1$, and passing through the point $(0, 2)$.

06 2016 28

Graphing

1. A major car company analyzes its revenue, $R(x)$, and costs $C(x)$, in millions of dollars over a fifteen-year period. The company represents its revenue and costs as a function of time, in years, x, using the given functions.

08 2018 37

$$R(x) = 550x^3 - 12,000x^2 + 83,000x + 7000$$
$$C(x) = 880x^3 - 21,000x^2 + 150,000x - 160,000$$

The company's profits can be represented as the difference between its revenue and costs.

Write the profit function, $P(x)$, as a polynomial in standard form.

Graph $y = P(x)$ on the set of axes below over the domain $2 \leq x \leq 16$.

$P(x) = 550x^3 - 1200x^2 + 83000x + 7000$

$- C(x) = \left(-880x^3 + 21000x^2 - 150,000x + 160,000 \right)$

Graphing

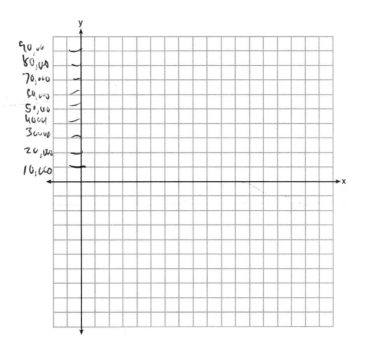

Over the given domain, state when the company was the least profitable and the most profitable, to the *nearest year*.

Explain how you determined your answer.

2. Graph $t(x) = 3\sin(2x) + 2$ over the domain $[0, 2\pi]$ on the set of axes below.

08 2018 30

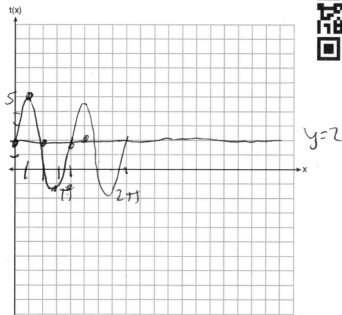

3. The parabola described by the equation $y = \frac{1}{12}(x-2)^2 + 2$ has the directrix at $y = -1$. The focus of the parabola is

08 2018 23

1) $(2, -1)$ 3) $(2, 3)$

2) $(2, 2)$ 4) $(2, 5)$

4. Which function's graph has a period of 8 and reaches a maximum height of 1 if at least one full period is graphed?

08 2018 20

1) $y = -4\cos\left(\dfrac{\pi}{4}x\right) - 3$

3) $y = -4\cos(8x) - 3$

2) $y = -4\cos\left(\dfrac{\pi}{4}x\right) + 5$

4) $y = -4\cos(8x) + 5$

5. The graph below represents national and New York State average gas prices.

08 2018 17

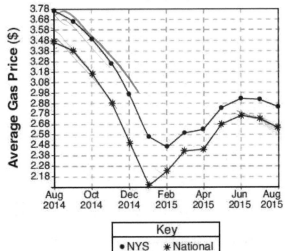

If New York State's gas prices are modeled by $G(x)$ and $C > 0$, which expression best approximates the national average x months from August 2014?

1) $G(x + C)$

3) $G(x - C)$

2) $G(x) + C$

4) $G(x) - C$

60

6.   Which sketch best represents the graph of
      $x = 3^y$?

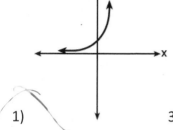

08 2018 16

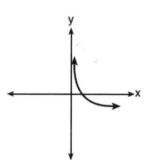

1)

3)

2)

4)

7.   Website popularity ratings are often
      determined using models that incorporate
      the number of visits per week a website
      receives. One model for ranking websites is
      $P(x) = \log(x - 4)$, where x is the
      number of visits per week in thousands and
      $P(x)$ is the website's popularity rating. According
      to this model, if a website is visited 16,000 times

06 2018 37

$P(x) = \log(15996)$
4.2

$P(x) = \log(x-4)$
$P(x) = \log(16,000-4)$

in one week, what is its popularity rating, rounded to the *nearest tenth*?

Graph $y = P(x)$ on the axes below.

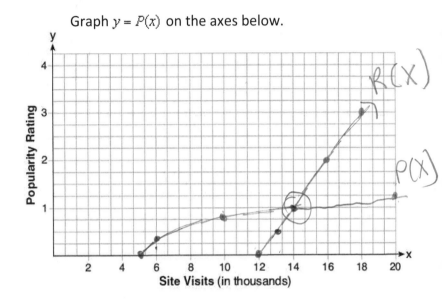

An alternative rating model is represented by $R(x) = \frac{1}{2}x - 6$, where x is the number of visits per week in thousands. Graph $R(x)$ on the same set of axes. For what number of weekly visits will the two models provide the same rating?

14,000

8. On the grid below, graph the function $f(x) = x^3 - 6x^2 + 9x + 6$ on the domain $-1 \le x \le 4$.

06 2018 26

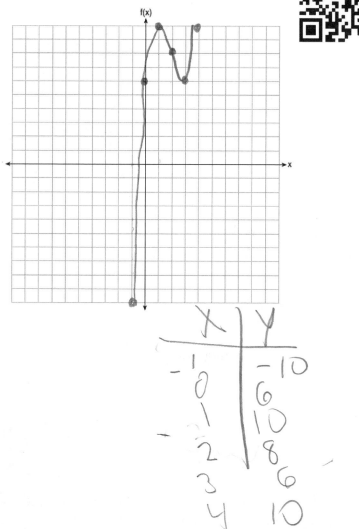

x	y
-1	-10
0	6
1	10
2	8
3	6
4	10

9. A 4th degree polynomial has zeros -5, 3, i, and $-i$. Which graph could represent the function defined by this polynomial?

06 2018 16

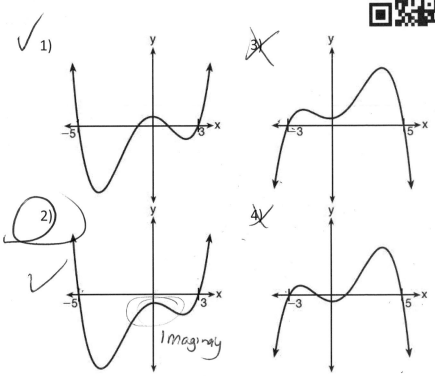

1)

2)

Imaginary

3)

4)

10. Graph $y = \log_2(x + 3) - 5$ a set of axes. Use an appropriate scale to include *both* intercepts.

Describe the behavior of the given function as *x* approaches -3 and as *x* approaches positive infinity.

06 2017 35

11. Graph $y = 400(.85)^{2x} - 6$ on the set of axes below.

06 2017 29

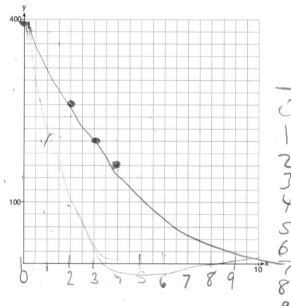

X	Y
0	394
1	283
2	282
3	144.8
4	183
5	72.75
6	50.89
7	35.10
8	23.7
9	15.4
10	9.5

12. If $f(x) = 3|x| - 1$ and $g(x) = 0.03x^3 - x + 1$, an approximate solution for the equation $f(x) = g(x)$ is

06 2017 05

1)   1.96   3)   (−0.99, 1.96)

2)   11.29   4)   (11.29, 32.87)

$3|x| - 1 = 0.03x^3 - x + 1$

65

13. The graph of the function $p(x)$ is sketched below.

06 2017 01

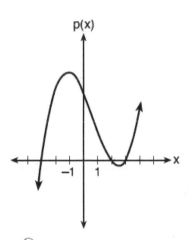

Which equation could represent $p(x)$?

1) $p(x) = (x^2 - 9)(x - 2)$

2) $p(x) = x^3 - 2x^2 + 9x + 18$

3) $p(x) = (x^2 + 9)(x - 2)$

4) $p(x) = x^3 + 2x^2 - 9x - 18$

14. To the *nearest tenth*, the value of x that satisfies $2^x = -2x + 11$ is

08 2016 03

1) 2.5 3) 5.8

2) 2.6 4) 5.9

$2^x = -2x + 11$

15. Sally's high school is planning their spring musical. The revenue, R, generated can be determined by the function
$R(t) = -33t^2 + 360t$, where t represents the price of a ticket. The production cost, C, of the musical is represented by the function
$C(t) = 700 + 5t.$

What is the highest ticket price, to the *nearest dollar*, they can charge in order to *not* lose money on the event?

1) $t = 3$ 3) $t = 8$

2) $t = 5$ 4) $t = 11$

$R(t) = -33t^2 + 360t$

16. Which equation represents the set of points equidistant from line ℓ and point R shown on the graph below?

08 2016 19

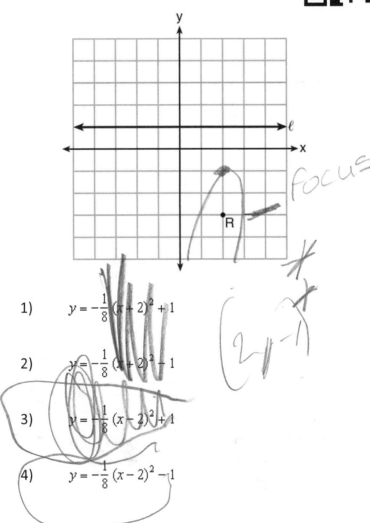

1) $y = -\dfrac{1}{8}(x+2)^2 + 1$

2) $y = -\dfrac{1}{8}(x+2)^2 - 1$

3) $y = \dfrac{1}{8}(x-2)^2 + 1$

4) $y = -\dfrac{1}{8}(x-2)^2 - 1$

17. Which graph has the following characteristics? 06 2016 04

- three real zeros
- as $x \to -\infty$, $f(x) \to -\infty$
- as $x \to \infty$, $f(x) \to \infty$

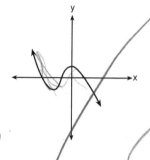

1)

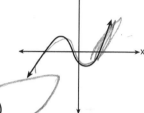

3)

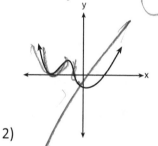

2)

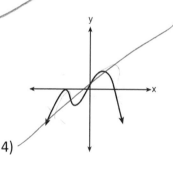

4)

18. Which statement about the graph of $c(x) = \log_6 x$ is *false*? 06 2016 18

1) The asymptote has equation $y = 0$.
2) The graph has no y-intercept.
3) The domain is the set of positive reals.
4) The range is the set of all real numbers.

19.   There was a study done on oxygen
       Consumption of snails as a function of pH,
       and the result was a degree 4 polynomial
       function whose graph is shown below.

06 2016 20

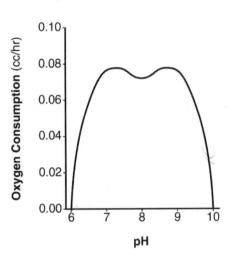

Which statement about this function is *incorrect*?

1)   The degree of the polynomial is even.

2)   There is a positive leading coefficient.

3)   At two pH values, there is a relative
      maximum value.

4)   There are two intervals where the
      function is decreasing.

Functions

1. If $p(x) = 2\ln(x) - 1$ and $m(x) = \ln(x + 6)$, then what is the solution for $p(x) = m(x)$?

08 2018 19

1) 1.65   3) 5.62

2) 3.14   4) no solution

2.. Given $f(x) = \dfrac{1}{2}x + 8$, which equation represents the inverse, $g(x)$?

08 2018 06

1) $g(x) = 2x - 8$ 3) $g(x) = -\dfrac{1}{2}x + 8$

2) $g(x) = 2x - 16$ 4) $g(x) = -\dfrac{1}{2}x - 16$

3. What is the inverse of $f(x) = x^3 - 2$?

06 2018 15

1) $f^{-1}(x) = \sqrt[3]{x} + 2$ 3) $f^{-1}(x) = \sqrt[3]{x + 2}$

2) $f^{-1}(x) = \pm\sqrt[3]{x} + 2$ 4) $f^{-1}(x) = \pm\sqrt[3]{x + 2}$

Functions

4. Which function is even?

06 2018 06

1) $f(x) = \sin x$ 3) $f(x) = |x - 2| + 5$

2) $f(x) = x^2 - 4$ 4) $f(x) = x^4 + 3x^3 + 4$

5. Algebraically determine whether the function $j(x) = x^4 - 3x^2 - 4$ is odd, even, or neither.

08 2017 31

6. The inverse of the function $f(x) = \dfrac{x+1}{x-2}$ is

08 2017 14

1) $f^{-1}(x) = \dfrac{x+1}{x+2}$ 3) $f^{-1}(x) = \dfrac{x+1}{x-2}$

2) $f^{-1}(x) = \dfrac{2x+1}{x-1}$ 4) $f^{-1}(x) = \dfrac{x-1}{x+1}$

7. The function $f(x) = \dfrac{x-3}{x^2 + 2x - 8}$ is undefined when x equals

08 2017 01

1) 2 or −4   3) 3, only

2) 4 or −2   4) 2, only

8. The function $f(x) = 2^{-0.25x} \cdot \sin\left(\dfrac{\pi}{2} x\right)$ represents a damped sound wave function. What is the average, rate of change for this function on the interval $[-7, 7]$ to the *nearest hundredth*?

06 2017 21

1) -3.66

3) -0.26

2) -0.30

4) 3.36

9. Which equation represents an odd function?

08 2016 14

1) $y = \sin x$

3) $y = (x + 1)^3$

2) $y = \cos x$

4) $y = e^{5x}$

10. The *x*-value of which function's *x*-intercept is larger, *f* or *h*? Justify your answer.

08 2016 30

$$f(x) = \log(x - 4)$$

x	h(x)
−1	6
0	4
1	2
2	0
3	−2

11. The distance needed to stop a car after applying the brakes varies directly with the square of the car's speed. The table below shows stopping distances for various speeds.

08 2016 31

Speed (mph)	10	20	30	40	50	60	70
Distance (ft)	6.25	25	56.25	100	156.25	225	306.25

Determine the average rate of change in braking distance, in ft/mph, between one car traveling at 50 mph and one traveling at 70 mph.

Explain what this rate of change means as it relates to braking distance

12. If $g(c) = 1 - c^2$ and $m(c) = c + 1$, then which statement is *not* true?

06 2016 08

1) $g(c) \cdot m(c) = 1 + c - c^2 - c^3$

2) $g(c) + m(c) = 2 + c - c^2$

3) $m(c) - g(c) = c + c^2$

4) $\dfrac{m(c)}{g(c)} = \dfrac{-1}{1 - c}$

13. Given $f^{-1}(x) = -\dfrac{3}{4}x + 2$, which equation represents $f(x)$?

06 2016 16

1) $f(x) = \dfrac{4}{3}x - \dfrac{8}{3}$

2) $f(x) = -\dfrac{4}{3}x + \dfrac{8}{3}$

3) $f(x) = \dfrac{3}{4}x - 2$

4) $f(x) = -\dfrac{3}{4}x + 2$

14. The equation $4x^2 - 24x + 4y^2 + 72y = 76$ is equivalent to

06 2016 19

1) $4(x - 3)^2 + 4(y + 9)^2 = 76$

2) $4(x - 3)^2 + 4(y + 9)^2 = 121$

3) $4(x - 3)^2 + 4(y + 9)^2 = 166$

4) $4(x - 3)^2 + 4(y + 9)^2 = 436$

Systems of Equations

1. Solve the following system of equations algebraically for all values of x, y, and z:

    08 2018 33

    $$2x + 3y - 4z = -1$$
    $$x - 2y + 5z = 3$$
    $$-4x + y + z = 16$$

2. Solve the following system of equations algebraically.

    08 2018 31

    $$x^2 + y^2 = 400$$
    $$y = x - 28$$

3. Consider the system shown below.

    08 2017 19

    $$2x - y = 4$$
    $$(x + 3)^2 + y^2 = 8$$

    The two solutions of the system can be described as

    1) both imaginary   3) both rational

    2) both irrational   4) one rational and
                                one irrational

4. Solve the following system of equations algebraically for all values of x, y, and z:

06 2017 33

$$x + y + z = 1$$
$$2x + 4y + 6z = 2$$
$$-x + 3y - 5z = 11$$

5. Which value is *not* contained in the solution of the system shown below?

08 2016 23

$$a + 5b - c = -20$$
$$4a - 5b + 4c = 19$$
$$-a - 5b - 5c = 2$$

1) -2 3) 3

2) 2 4) -3

6. Solve the system of equations shown below algebraically.

06 2016 33

$$(x - 3)^2 + (y + 2)^2 = 16$$
$$2x + 2y = 10$$

Sequences and Series

1. The recursive formula to describe a sequence is shown below.

   06 2018 30

   $$a_1 = 3$$

   $$a_n = 1 + 2a_{n-1}$$

   State the first four terms of this sequence. Can this sequence be represented using an explicit geometric formula? Justify your answer.

2. Simon lost his library card and has an overdue library book. When the book was 5 days late, he owed $2.25 to replace his library card and pay the fine for the overdue book. When the book was 21 days late, he owed $6.25 to replace his library card and pay the fine for the overdue book. Suppose the total amount Simon owes when the book is n days late can be determined by an arithmetic sequence.

   08 2017 34

   Determine a formula for a_n, the nth term of this sequence. Use the formula to determine the amount of money, in dollars, Simon needs to pay when the book is 60 days late.

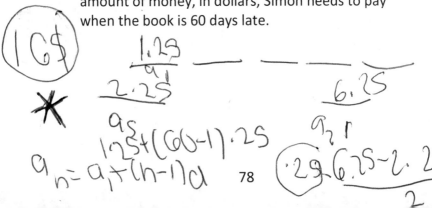

3. While experimenting with her calculator, Candy creates the sequence
4, 9, 19, 39, 79, ...

08 2017 29

Write a recursive formula for Candy's sequence. Determine the eighth term in Candy's sequence.

4. The Rickerts decided to set up an account for their daughter to pay for her college education. The day their daughter was born, they deposited $1000 in an account that pays 1.8% compounded annually. Beginning with her first birthday, they deposit an additional $750 into the account on each of her birthdays.

08 2017 24

Which expression correctly represents the amount of money in the account n years after their daughter was born?

1) $a_n = 1000(1.018)^n + 750$

3) $a_0 = 1000$
$a_n = a_{n-1}(1.018) + 750$

2) $a_n = 1000(1.018)^n + 750n$

4) $a_0 = 1000$
$a_n = a_{n-1}(1.018) + 750n$

$a_0 = 1000$

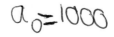

5. A ball is dropped from a height of 32 feet. It bounces and rebounds 80% of the height from which it was falling. What is the total downward distance, in feet, the ball traveled up to the 12th bounce?

08 2017 21

1) 29

3) 120

2) 58

4) 149

6. Given $f(9) = -2$, which function can be used to generate the sequence
$$-8, -7.25, -6.5, -5.75, \ldots ?$$

06 2017 20

1) $f(n) = -8 + 0.75n$

2) $f(n) = -8 - 0.75(n - 1)$

3) $f(n) = -8.75 + 0.75n$

4) $f(n) = -0.75 + 8(n - 1)$

7. A recursive formula for the sequence $18, 9, 4.5, \ldots$ is

08 2016 08

1) $g_1 = 18$

$g_n = \dfrac{1}{2} g_{n-1}$

2) $g_n = 18 \left(\dfrac{1}{2} \right)^{n-1}$

3) $g_1 = 18$

$g_n = 2 g_{n-1}$

4) $g_n = 18(2)^{n-1}$

8. Kristin wants to increase her running endurance. According to experts, a gradual mileage increase of 10% per week can reduce the risk of injury. If Kristin runs 8 miles in week one, which expression can help her find the total number of miles she will have run over the course of her 6-week training program?

08 2016 09

1) $\displaystyle\sum_{n=1}^{6} 8(1.10)^{n-1}$

2) $\displaystyle\sum_{n=1}^{6} 8(1.10)^{n}$

3) $\dfrac{8 - 8(1.10)^{6}}{0.90}$

4) $\dfrac{8 - 8(0.10)^{n}}{1.10}$

9. The sequence $a_1 = 6, a_n = 3a_{n-1}$ can also be written as

08 2016 18

1) $a_n = 6 \cdot 3^n$

2) $a_n = 6 \cdot 3^{n+1}$

3) $a_n = 2 \cdot 3^n$

4) $a_n = 2 \cdot 3^{n+1}$

10. The formula below can be used to model which scenario?

06 2016 10

$$a_1 = 3000$$

$$a_n = 0.80a_{n-1}$$

1) The first row of a stadium has 3000 seats, and each row thereafter has 80 more seats than the row in front of it.

2) The last row of a stadium has 3000 seats, and each row before it has 80 fewer seats than the row behind it.

3) A bank account starts with a deposit of $3000, and each year it grows by 80%.

4) The initial value of a specialty toy is $3000, and its value each of the following years is 20% less.

11. The population of Jamesburg for the years 2010-2013, respectively, was reported as follows:

06 2016 23

250,000   250,937   251,878   252,822

How can this sequence be recursively modeled?

1) $j_n = 250,000(1.00375)^{n-1}$

2) $j_n = 250,000 + 937^{(n-1)}$

3) $j_1 = 250,000$
   $j_n = 1.00375j_{n-1}$

4) $j_1 = 250,000$
   $j_n = j_{n-1} + 937$

Probability

1. A fast-food restaurant analyzes data to better serve its customers. After its analysis, it discovers that the events D, that a customer uses the drive-thru, and F, that a customer orders French fries, are independent.

The following data are given in a report:

$$P(F) = 0.8$$
$$P(F \cap D) = 0.456$$

Given this information, $P(F|D)$ is

1) 0.344   3) 0.57

2) 0.3648   4) 0.8

2. Data for the students enrolled in a local high school are shown in the Venn diagram below.

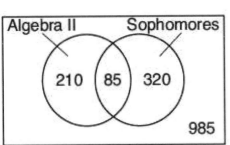

If a student from the high school is selected at random, what is the probability that the student is a sophomore given that the student is enrolled in Algebra II?

1) $\dfrac{85}{210}$ 3) $\dfrac{85}{405}$

2) $\dfrac{85}{295}$ 4) $\dfrac{85}{1600}$

3. A survey about television-viewing preferences was given to randomly selected freshmen and seniors at Fairport High School. The results are shown in the table below.

06 2018 25

Favorite Type of Program			
	Sports	Reality Show	Comedy Series
Senior	83	110	67
Freshmen	119	103	54

A student response is selected at random from the results. State the *exact* probability the student response is from a freshman, given the student prefers to watch reality shows on television.

4.   On a given school day, the probability
        that Nick oversleeps is 48% and the
        probability he has a pop quiz is 25%.
        Assuming these two events are
        independent, what is the probability that
        Nick oversleeps and has a pop quiz on
        the same day?

06 2018 11

1) 73%   3) 23%

2) 36%   4) 12%

5.   A study was designed to test the
        effectiveness of a new drug. Half of
        the volunteers received the drug.
        The other half received a sugar pill.
        The probability of a volunteer receiving
        the drug and getting well was 40%.
        What is the probability of a volunteer
        getting well, given that the volunteer
        received the drug?

08 2017 26

6. Data collected about jogging from students with two older siblings are shown in the table below.

06 2017 32

	Neither Sibling Jogs	One Sibling Jogs	Both Siblings Jog
Student Does Not Jog	1168	1823	1380
Student Jogs	188	416	400

Using these data, determine whether a student with two older siblings is more likely to jog if one sibling jogs or if both siblings jog. Justify your answer.

7. The probability that Gary and Jane have a child with blue eyes is 0.25, and the probability that they have a child with blond hair is 0.5. The probability that they have a child with both blue eyes and blond hair is 0.125. Given this information, the events blue eyes and blond hair are

06 2017 14

    I: dependent
    II: independent
    III: mutually exclusive

1) I, only   3) I and III

2) II, only   4) II and III

8. The set of data in the table below shows the results of a survey on the number of messages that people of different ages text on their cell phones each month.

08 2016 07

Age Group	Text Messages per Month		
	0–10	11–50	Over 50
15–18	4	37	68
19–22	6	25	87
23–60	25	47	157

If a person from this survey is selected at random, what is the probability that the person texts over 50 messages per month given that the person is between the ages of 23 and 60?

1) $\dfrac{157}{229}$
2) $\dfrac{157}{312}$

3) $\dfrac{157}{384}$
4) $\dfrac{157}{456}$

9. Given events A and B, such that $P(A) = 0.6$, $P(B) = 0.5$, and $P(A \cup B) = 0.8$, determine whether A and B are independent or dependent.

08 2016 32

10. Sean's team has a baseball game tomorrow. He pitches 50% of the games. There is a 40% chance of rain during the game tomorrow. If the probability that it rains given that Sean pitches is 40%, it can be concluded that these two events are

06 2016 11

1) independent 3) mutually exclusive

2) dependent 4) complements

11. A suburban high school has a population of 1376 students. The number of students who participate in sports is 649. The number of students who participate in music is 433. If the probability that a student participates in either sports or music is $\frac{974}{1376}$, what is the probability that a student participates in both sports and music?

06 2016 29

Statistics

1.   To determine if the type of music played
      while taking a quiz has a relationship to
      results, 16 students were randomly
      assigned to either a room softly playing
      classical music or a room softly playing rap
      music. The results on the quiz were
      as follows:

08 2018 36

Classical: 74, 83, 77, 77, 84, 82, 90, 89
Rap: 77, 80, 78, 74, 69, 72, 78, 69

John correctly rounded the difference of the means of his
experimental groups as 7. How did John obtain this value and
what does it represent in the given context?

Justify your answer. To determine if there is any significance in
this value, John rerandomized the 16 scores into two groups of 8,
calculated the difference of the means, and simulated this process
250 times as shown below.

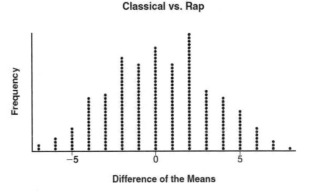

Classical vs. Rap

Does the simulation support the theory that there may be a
significant difference in quiz scores? Explain.

2. Some smart-phone applications contain "in-app" purchases, which allow users to purchase special content within the application. A random sample of 140 users found that 35 percent made in-app purchases. A simulation was conducted with 200 samples of 140 users assuming 35 percent of the samples make in-app purchases. The approximately normal results are shown below.

08 2018 32

Mean = 0.350
SD = 0.042

Proportion of In-App Purchases

Considering the middle 95% of the data, determine the margin of error, to the *nearest hundredth*, for the simulated results. In the given context, explain what this value represents.

3.   The scores of a recent test taken by 1200 students had an approximately normal distribution with a mean of 225 and a standard deviation of 18.

08 2018 28

Determine the number of students who scored between 200 and 245.

4.   A researcher randomly divides 50 bean plants into two groups. He puts one group by a window to receive natural light and the second group under artificial light. He records the growth of the plants weekly. Which data collection method is described in this situation?

08 2018 02

   1) observational study   3) survey

   2) controlled experiment   4) systematic sample

5.   Joseph was curious to determine if scent improves memory. A test was created where better memory is indicated by higher test scores. A controlled experiment was performed where one group was given the test on scented paper and the other group was given the test on unscented paper.
The summary statistics from the experiment are given below.

06 2018 34

	Scented Paper	Unscented Paper
$\overline{x}$	23	18
S_x	2.898	2.408

Calculate the difference in means in the experimental test grades (scented -unscented). A simulation was conducted in which the subjects' scores were rerandomized into two groups 1000 times. The differences of the group means were calculated each time. The results are shown below.

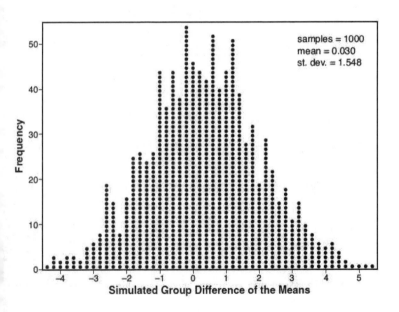

samples = 1000
mean = 0.030
st. dev. = 1.548

Simulated Group Difference of the Means

Use the simulation results to determine the interval representing the middle 95% of the difference in means, to the *nearest hundredth*. Is the difference in means in Joseph's experiment statistically significant based on the simulation? Explain.

6. Chuck's Trucking Company has decided to initiate an Employee of the Month program. To determine the recipient, they put the following sign on the back of each truck.

06 2018 28

How's My Driving?

Call 1-555-DRIVING

The driver who receives the highest number of positive comments will win the recognition.

Explain *one* statistical bias in this data collection method.

7. The weights of bags of Graseck's Chocolate Candies are normally distributed with a mean of 4.3 ounces and a standard deviation of 0.05 ounces. What is the probability that a bag of these chocolate candies weighs less than 4.27 ounces?

06 2018 17

1) 0.2257   3) 0.7257

2) 0.2743   4) 0.7757

8. Mrs. Jones had hundreds of jelly beans in a bag that contained equal numbers of six different flavors. Her student randomly selected four jelly beans and they were all black licorice. Her student complained and said "What are the odds I got all of that kind?" Mrs. Jones replied, "simulate rolling a die 250 times and tell me if four black licorice jelly beans is unusual." Explain how this simulation could be used to solve the problem.

08 2017 28

9. A public opinion poll was conducted on behalf of Mayor Ortega's reelection campaign shortly before the election. 264 out of 550 likely voters said they would vote for Mayor Ortega; the rest said they would vote for his opponent. Which statement is *least* appropriate to make, according to the results of the poll?

08 2017 22

1) There is a 48% chance that Mayor Ortega will win the election.

2) The point estimate $(\hat{p})$ of voters who will vote for Mayor Ortega is 48%.

3) It is most likely that between 44% and 52% of voters will vote for Mayor Ortega.

4) Due to the margin of error, an inference cannot be made regarding whether Mayor Ortega or his opponent is most likely to win the election.

10. Which scenario is best described as an observational study?

08 2017 17

1) For a class project, students in Health class ask every tenth student entering the school if they eat breakfast in the morning.

3) A researcher wants to learn whether or not there is a link between children's daily amount of physical activity and their overall energy level. During lunch at the local high school, she distributed a short questionnaire to students in the cafeteria.

2) A social researcher wants to learn whether or not there is a link between attendance and grades. She gathers data from 15 school districts.

4) Sixty seniors taking a course in Advanced Algebra Concepts are randomly divided into two classes. One class uses a graphing calculator all the time, and the other class never uses graphing calculators. A guidance counselor wants to determine whether there is link between graphing calculator use and students' final exam grades.

11. A study conducted in 2004 in New York City found that 212 out of 1334 participants had hypertension. Kim ran a simulation of 100 studies based on these data. The output of the simulation is shown in the diagram below.

08 2017 16

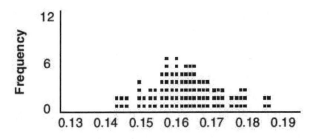

At a 95% confidence level, the proportion of New York City residents with hypertension and the margin of error are closest to

1) proportion $\approx .16$; margin of error $\approx .01$

2) proportion $\approx .16$; margin of error $\approx .02$

3) proportion $\approx .01$; margin of error $\approx .16$

4) proportion $\approx .02$; margin of error $\approx .16$

12. The distribution of the diameters of ball Bearings made under a given manufacturing process is normally distributed with a mean of 4 cm and a standard deviation of 0.2 cm. What proportion of the ball bearings will have a diameter less than 3.7 cm?

08 2017 11

   1) 0.0668   3) 0.8664

   2) 0.4332   4) 0.9500

13. Charlie's Automotive Dealership is considering implementing a new check-in procedure for customers who are bringing their vehicles for routine maintenance. The dealership will launch the procedure if 50% or more of the customers give the new procedure a favorable rating when compared to the current procedure. The dealership devises a simulation based on the minimal requirement that 50% of the customers prefer the new procedure. Each dot on the graph below represents the proportion of the customers who preferred the new check-in procedure, each of sample size 40, simulated 100 times.

06 2017 36

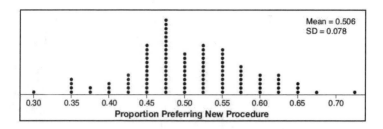

Assume the set of data is approximately normal and the dealership wants to be 95% confident of its results.

Determine an interval containing the plausible sample values for which the dealership will launch the new procedure. Round your answer to the *nearest hundredth*.

Forty customers are selected randomly to undergo the new check-in procedure and the proportion of customers who prefer the new procedure is 32.5%. The dealership decides *not* to implement the new check-in procedure based on the results of the study.

Use statistical evidence to explain this decision.

14. The weight of a bag of pears at the local market averages 8 pounds with a standard deviation of 0.5 pound. The weights of all the bags of pears at the market closely follow a normal distribution.

06 2017 26

Determine what percentage of bags, to the *Nearest integer*, weighed *less* than 8.25 pounds.

15. A game spinner is divided into 6 equally sized 06 2017 10 regions, as shown in the diagram below.

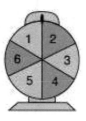

For Miles to win, the spinner must land on the number 6. After spinning the spinner 10 times, and losing all 10 times, Miles complained that the spinner is unfair. At home, his dad ran 100 simulations of spinning the spinner 10 times, assuming the probability of winning each spin is $\frac{1}{6}$. The output of the simulation is shown in the diagram below.

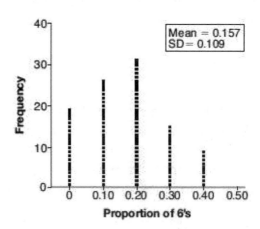

Which explanation is appropriate for Miles and his dad to make?

1) The spinner was likely unfair, since the number 6 to occur in about 20% of the simulations.

2) The spinner was likely unfair, since the spinner should have landed on the number 6 by the sixth spin.

3) The spinner was likely not unfair, since the number 6 failed to occur in about 20% of the simulations.

4) The spinner was likely not unfair, since in the output the player wins once or twice in the majority of the simulations.

16. Cheap and Fast gas station is conducting a consumer satisfaction survey. Which method of collecting data would most likely lead to a biased sample?

06 2017 03

1) interviewing every 5th customer to come into the station

2) interviewing customers chosen at random by a computer at the checkout

3) interviewing customers who call an 800 number posted on the customers' receipts

4) interviewing every customer who comes into the station on a day of the week chosen at random out of a hat

17.   Which statement(s) about statistical studies is true?

08 2016 02

I. A survey of all English classes in a high school would be a good sample to determine the number of hours students throughout the school spend studying.

II.   A survey of all ninth graders in a high school would be a good sample to determine the number of student parking spaces needed at that high school.

III.   A survey of all students in one lunch period in a high school would be a good sample to determine the number of hours adults spend on social media websites.

IV. A survey of all Calculus students in a high school would be a good sample to determine the number of students throughout the school who don't like math.

1)   I, only   2)   II, only

3)   I and III   4)   III and IV

18. The lifespan of a 60-watt light bulb produced by a company is normally distributed with a mean of 1450 hours and a standard deviation of 8.5 hours. If a 60-watt lightbulb produced by this company is selected at random, what is the probability that its lifespan will be between 1440 and 1465 hours?

08 2016 04

1)   0.3803   2)   0.4612

3)   0.8415   4)   0.9612

19. A candidate for political office commissioned a poll. His staff received responses from 900 likely voters and 55% of them said they would vote for the candidate. The staff then conducted a simulation of 1000 more polls of 900 voters, assuming that 55% of voters would vote for their candidate. The output of the simulation is shown in the diagram below.

08 2016 12

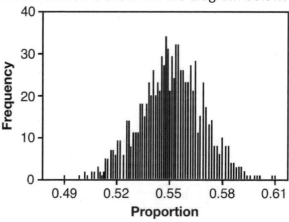

Given this output, and assuming a 95% confidence level, the margin of error for the poll is closest to

1)   0.01   2)   0.03

3)   0.06   4)   0.12

20.   Elizabeth waited for 6 minutes at the drive thru at her favorite fast-food restaurant the last time she visited. She was upset about having to wait that long and notified the manager. The manager assured her that her experience was very unusual and that it would not happen again. A study of customers commissioned by this restaurant found an approximately normal distribution of results. The mean wait time was 226 seconds and the standard deviation was 38 seconds.

08 2016 29

Given these data, and using a 95% level of confidence, was Elizabeth's wait time unusual?

Justify your answer.

21. Ayva designed an experiment to determine the effect of a new energy drink on a group of 20 volunteer students. Ten students were randomly selected to form group 1 while the remaining 10 made up group 2. Each student in group 1 drank one energy drink, and each student in group 2 drank one cola drink. Ten minutes later, their times were recorded for reading the same paragraph of a novel. The results of the experiment are shown below.

08 2016 36

Group 1 (seconds)	Group 2 (seconds)
17.4	23.3
18.1	18.8
18.2	22.1
19.6	12.7
18.6	16.9
16.2	24.4
16.1	21.2
15.3	21.2
17.8	16.3
19.7	14.5
Mean = 17.7	Mean = 19.1

Ayva thinks drinking energy drinks makes students read faster. Using information from the experimental design or the results, explain why Ayva's hypothesis may be *incorrect*. Using the given results, Ayva randomly mixes the 20 reading times, splits them into two groups of 10, and simulates the difference of the means 232 times.

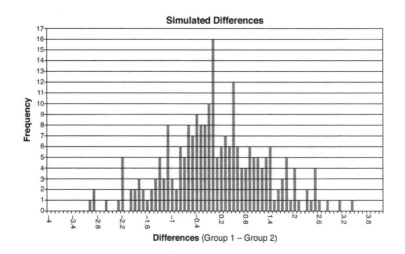

Ayva has decided that the difference in mean reading times is not an unusual occurrence.

Support her decision using the results of the simulation.

Explain your reasoning.

22. Julie averaged 85 on the first three tests of the semester in her mathematics class. If she scores 93 on each of the remaining tests, her average will be 90.

06 2016 02

Which equation could be used to determine how many tests, T, are left in the semester?

1) $\dfrac{255 + 93T}{3T} = 90$

2) $\dfrac{255 + 90T}{3T} = 93$

3) $\dfrac{255 + 93T}{T + 3} = 90$

4) $\dfrac{255 + 90T}{T + 3} = 93$

23. Anne has a coin. She does not know if it is a fair coin. She flipped the coin 100 times and obtained 73 heads and 27 tails. She ran a computer simulation of 200 samples of 100 fair coin flips. The output of the proportion of heads is shown below.

06 2016 07

Samples = 200
Mean = 0.497
SD = 0.050

Given the results of her coin flips and of her computer simulation, which statement is most accurate?

1) 73 of the computer's next 100 coin flips will be heads.

2) 50 of her next 100 coin flips will be heads.

3) Her coin is not fair.

4) Her coin is fair.

24. The heights of women in the United States are normally distributed with a mean of 64 inches and a standard deviation of 2.75 inches. The percent of women whose heights are between 64 and 69.5 inches, to the *nearest whole percent*, is

06 2016 09

1)	6	2)	48
3)	68	4)	95

25. Describe how a controlled experiment can be created to examine the effect of ingredient *X* in a toothpaste.

06 2016 26

26. Fifty-five students attending the prom were randomly selected to participate in a survey about the music choice at the prom. Sixty percent responded that a DJ would be preferred over a band. Members of the prom committee thought that the vote would have 50% for the DJ and 50% for the band. A simulation was run 200 times, each of sample size 55, based on the premise that 60% of the students would prefer a DJ. The approximate normal simulation results are shown below.

06 2016 35

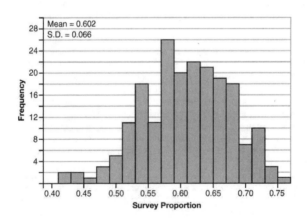

Using the results of the simulation, determine a plausible interval containing the middle 95% of the data. Round all values to the *nearest hundredth*. Members of the prom committee are concerned that a vote of all students attending the prom may produce a 50% – 50% split. Explain what statistical evidence supports this concern.

The University of the State of New York
REGENTS HIGH SCHOOL EXAMINATION

ALGEBRA II

Friday, June 21, 2019 - 1:15 to 4:15 p.m., only

Student Name _____

School Name _____

The possession or use of any communications device is strictly prohibited when taking this examination. If you have or use any communications device, no matter how briefly, your examination will be invalidated and no score will be calculated for you.

Print your name and the name of your school on the lines above. A separate answer sheet for **Part I** has been provided to you. Follow the instructions from the proctor for completing the student information on your answer sheet. This examination has four parts, with a total of 37 questions. You must answer all questions in this examination. Record your answers to the Part I multiple-choice questions on the separate answer sheet. Write your answers to the questions in **Parts II, III,** and **IV** directly in this booklet. All work should be written in pen, except for graphs and drawings, which should be done in pencil. Clearly indicate the necessary steps, including appropriate formula substitutions, diagrams, graphs, charts, etc. Utilize the information provided for each question to determine your answer. Note that diagrams are not necessarily drawn to scale. The formulas that you may need to answer some questions in this examination are found at the end of the examination. This sheet is perforated so you may remove it from this booklet. Scrap paper is not permitted for any part of this examination, but you may use the blank spaces in this booklet as scrap paper. A perforated sheet of scrap graph paper is provided at the end of this booklet for any question for which graphing may be helpful but is not required. You may remove this sheet from this booklet. Any work done on this sheet of scrap graph paper will not be scored. When you have completed the examination, you must sign the statement printed at the end of the answer sheet, indicating that you had no unlawful knowledge of the questions or answers prior to the examination and that you have neither given nor received assistance in answering any of the questions during the examination. Your answer sheet cannot be accepted if you fail to sign this

Notice …
A graphing calculator and a straightedge (ruler) must be available for you to use while taking this examination.

DO NOT OPEN THIS EXAMINATION BOOKLET UNTIL THE SIGNAL IS GIVEN.

Part I

Answer all 24 questions in this part. Each correct answer will receive 2 credits. No partial credit will be allowed. Utilize the information provided for each question to determine your answer. Note that diagrams are not necessarily drawn to scale. For each statement or question, choose the word or expression that, of those given, best completes the statement or answers the question. Record your answers on your separate answer sheet. [48]

1. A sociologist reviews randomly selected Surveillance videos from a public park over a period of several years and records the amount of time people spent on a smartphone. The statistical procedure the sociologist used is called

06 2019 01

1) a census
2) an experiment
3) an observational study
4) a sample survey

2. Which statement(s) are true for all real numbers?

I $(x-y)^2 = x^2 + y^2$
II $(x+y)^3 = x^3 + 3xy + y^3$

06 2019 02

1) I, only
2) II, only
3) I and II
4) neither I nor II

3. What is the solution set of the following system of equations?

$$y = 3x + 6$$

$$y = (x+4)^2 - 10$$

06 2019 03

1) $\{(-5,-9)\}$
2) $\{(5,21)\}$
3) $\{(0,6),(-5,-9)\}$
4) $\{(0,6),(5,21)\}$

4. Irma initially ran one mile in over ten minutes. She then began a training program to reduce her one-mile time. She recorded her one-mile time once a week for twelve consecutive weeks, as modeled in the graph below.

06 2019 04

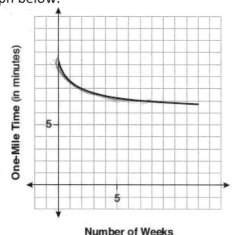

Number of Weeks

Which statement regarding Irma's one-mile training program is correct?

1) Her one-mile speed increased as the number of weeks increased.

2) Her one-mile speed decreased as the number of weeks increased.

3) If the trend continues, she will run under a six-minute mile by week thirteen.

4) She reduced her one-mile time the most between weeks ten and twelve.

5. A 7-year lease for office space states that the annual rent is $85,000 for the first year and will increase by 6% each additional year of the lease. What will the total rent expense be for the entire 7-year lease?

06 2019 05

1) $42,809.63   3) $595,000.00

2) $90,425.53   4) $713,476.20

8500

6. The graph of $y = f(x)$ is shown below.

06 2019 06

(6,40)

(4,20)

10

(2,10)

−2   1   8

Which expression defines $f(x)$?

1) $2x$

2) $5(2^x)$

3) $5(2^{\frac{x}{2}})$

4) $5(2^{2x})$

1^3 x^3-1

7. Given $P(x) = x^3 - 3x^2 - 2x + 4$, which statement is true?

06 2019 07

1) $(x - 1)$ is a factor because $P(-1) = 2$.

2) $(x + 1)$ is a factor because $P(-1) = 2$.

3) $(x + 1)$ is a factor because $P(1) = 0$.

4) $(x - 1)$ is a factor because $P(1) = 0$.

113

8. For $x \geq 0$, which equation is *false*?

06 2019 08

1) $(x^{\frac{3}{2}})^2 = \sqrt[3]{x^3}$

2) $(x^3)^{\frac{1}{4}} = \sqrt[4]{x^3}$

3) $(x^{\frac{3}{2}})^{\frac{1}{2}} = \sqrt[4]{x^3}$

4) $(x^{\frac{2}{3}})^2 = \sqrt[3]{x^4}$

9. What is the inverse of the function $y = 4x + 5$?

06 2019 09

1) $x = \frac{1}{4}y - \frac{5}{4}$

2) $y = \frac{1}{4}x - \frac{5}{4}$

3) $y = 4x - 5$

4) $y = \frac{1}{4x + 5}$

10. Which situation could be modeled using a geometric sequence?

06 2019 10

1) A cell phone company charges $30.00 per month for 2 gigabytes of data and $12.50 for each additional gigabyte of data.

3) David's parents have set a limit of 50 minutes per week that he may play online games during the school year. However, they will increase his time by 5% per week for the next ten weeks.

2) The temperature in your car is 79°. You lower the temperature of your air conditioning by 2° every 3 minutes in order to find a comfortable temperature.

4) Sarah has $100.00 in her piggy bank and saves an additional $15.00 each week.

11. The completely factored form of

$$n^4 - 9n^2 + 4n^3 - 36n - 12n^2 + 108 \text{ is}$$

06 2019 11

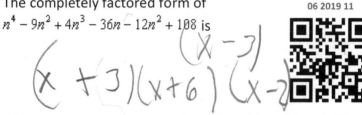

$(x - 7)$

$(x + 3)(x + 6)(x - 2)$

1) $(n^2 - 9)(n + 6)(n - 2)$ 3) $(n - 3)(n - 3)(n + 6)(n - 2)$

2) $(n + 3)(n - 3)(n + 6)(n - 2)$ 4) $(n + 3)(n - 3)(n - 6)(n + 2)$

12. What is the solution when the equation $wx^2 + w = 0$ is solved for x, where w is a positive integer?

06 2019 12

1) -1
2) 0

3) 6
4) $\pm i$

$$wx^2 + w = 0$$

$$2x^2 + 2 = 0$$

$$\sqrt{x^2} = \sqrt{-1}$$

$$wx^2 + w = 0$$
$$\quad -w \quad -w$$
$$\frac{wx^2}{w} = \frac{-w}{w}$$

115

13. A group of students was trying to determine the proportion of candies in a bag that are blue. The company claims that 24% of candies in bags are blue. A simulation was run 100 times with a sample size of 50, based on the premise that 24% of the candies are blue. The approximately normal results of the simulation are shown in the dot plot below.

06 2019 13

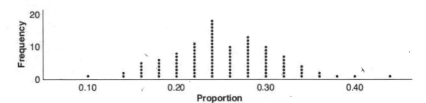

The simulation results in a mean of 0.254 and a standard deviation of 0.060. Based on this simulation, what is a plausible interval containing the middle 95% of the data?

1) (0.194, 0.314)   3) (−0.448, 0.568)
2) (0.134, 0.374)   4) (0.254, 0.374)

$$2 \times .060$$

$$0.374 - 0.134$$

14. Selected values for the functions f and g are shown in the tables below.

x	f(x)
−3.12	−4.88
0	−6
1.23	−4.77
8.52	2.53
9.01	3.01

x	g(x)
−2.01	−1.01
0	0.58
8.52	2.53
13.11	3.01
16.52	3.29

A solution to the equation $f(x) = g(x)$ is

1) 0   3) 3.01
2) 2.53   4) 8.52

15. The expression $6 - (3x - 2i)^2$ is equivalent to

1) $-9x^2 + 12xi + 10$ 3) $-9x^2 + 10$
2) $9x^2 - 12xi + 2$ 4) $-9x^2 + 12xi - 4i + 6$

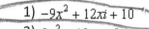

16. A number, minus twenty times its reciprocal, equals eight. The number is

1) 10 or −2   3) −10 or −2
2) 10 or 2   4) −10 or 2

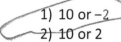

117

17. A savings account, S, has an initial value of $50. The account grows at a 2% interest rate compounded n times per year, t, according to the function below.

06 2019 17

$$S(t) = 50\left(1 + \frac{.02}{n}\right)^{nt}$$

Which statement about the account is correct?

1) As the value of n increases, the amount of interest per year decreases.

2) As the value of n increases, the value of the account approaches the function $S(t) = 50e^{0.02t}$.

3) As the value of n decreases to one, the amount of interest per year increases.

4) As the value of n decreases to one, the value of the account approaches the function $S(t) = 50(1 - 0.02)^t$.

18. There are 400 students in the senior class at Oak Creek High School. All of these students took the SAT. The distribution of their SAT scores is approximately normal. The number of students who scored within 2 standard deviations of the mean is approximately

06 2019 18

1) 75
2) 95

3) 300
4) 380

$.95(400)$

118

19. The solution set for the equation

$$b = \sqrt{2b^2 - 64} \text{ is}$$

1) {−8}   3) {±8}

2) {8}   4) { }

20. Which table best represents an exponential relationship?

1)

x	y
1	8
2	4
3	2
4	1
5	$\frac{1}{2}$

3)

x	y
0	0
1	1
2	4
3	9
4	16

2)

x	y
8	0
4	1
0	2
−4	3
−8	4

4)

x	y
1	1
2	8
3	27
4	64
5	125

ab^x

common ratios

119

21. A sketch of $r(x)$ is shown below.

06 2019 21

r(x)

-c   -b   a   x

An equation for $r(x)$ could be

1) $r(x) = (x-a)(x+b)(x+c)$ 3) $r(x) = (x+a)(x-b)(x-c)$

2) $r(x) = (x+a)(x-b)(x-c)^2$ 4) $r(x) = (x-a)(x+b)(x+c)^2$

22. The temperature, in degrees Fahrenheit, in Times Square during a day in August can be predicted by the function

06 2019 22

$$T(x) = 8\sin(0.3x - 3) + 74,$$

where *x* is the number of hours after midnight. According to this model, the predicted temperature, to the *nearest degree* Fahrenheit, at 7 P.M. is

1) 68   3) 77

2) 74   4) 81

23. Consider the system of equations below:

$$x + y - z = 6$$
$$2x - 3y + 2z = -19$$
$$-x + 4y - z = 17$$

Which number is *not* the value of any variable in the solution of the system?

1) −1

2) 2

3)

4)

3

−4

24. Camryn puts $400 into a savings account that earns 6% annually. The amount in her account can be modeled by $C(t) = 400(1.06)^t$ where t is the time in years.

Which expression best approximates the amount of money in her account using a weekly growth rate?

1) $400(1.001153846)^t$

2) $400(1.001121184)^t$

3) $400(1.001153846)^{52t}$

4) $400(1.001121184)^{52t}$

Part II

Answer all 8 questions in this part. Each correct answer will receive 2 credits. Clearly indicate the necessary steps, including appropriate formula substitutions, diagrams, graphs, charts, etc. Utilize the information provided for each question to determine your answer. Note that diagrams are not necessarily drawn to scale. For all questions in this part, a correct numerical answer with no work shown will receive only I credit. All answers should be written in pen, except for graphs and drawings, which should be done in pencil. [16]

25. The table below shows the number of hours of daylight on the first day of each month in Rochester, NY.

06 2019 25

Month	Hours of Daylight
Jan.	9.4
Feb.	10.6
March	11.9
April	13.9
May	14.7
June	15.4
July	15.1
Aug.	13.9
Sept.	12.5
Oct.	11.1
Nov.	9.7
Dec.	9.0

Given the data, what is the average rate of change in hours of daylight per month from January 1st to April 1st? Interpret what this means in the context of the problem.

24

26. Algebraically solve for x: $\dfrac{7}{2x} - \dfrac{2}{x+1} = \dfrac{1}{4}$

06 2019 26

27. Graph $f(x) = \log_2(x+6)$ on the set of axes below.

06 2019 27

28. Given $\tan \theta = \dfrac{7}{24}$, and θ terminates in Quadrant III, determine the value of $\cos \theta$.

06 2019 28

29. Kenzie believes that for $x \geq 0$, the expression $\left(\sqrt[7]{x^2}\right)\left(\sqrt[5]{x^3}\right)$ is equivalent to $\sqrt[35]{x^6}$.
Is she correct?
Justify your response algebraically.

06 2019 29

30. When the function $p(x)$ is divided by $x - 1$ the quotient is $x^2 + 7 + \dfrac{5}{x-1}$. State $p(x)$ in standard form.

06 2019 30

31. Write a recursive formula for the sequence $6, 9, 13.5, 20.25, \ldots$

06 2019 31

32. Robin flips a coin 100 times. It lands heads up 43 times, and she wonders if the coin is unfair. She runs a computer simulation of 750 samples of 100 fair coin flips.
The output of the proportion of heads is shown below.

06 2019 32

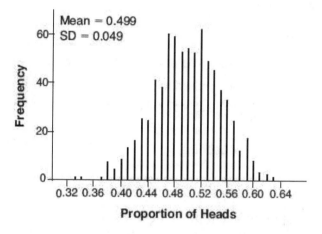

Mean = 0.499
SD = 0.049

Proportion of Heads

Do the results of the simulation provide strong evidence that Robin's coin is unfair? Explain your answer.

Part III

Answer all 4 questions in this part. Each correct answer will receive 4 credits. Clearly indicate the necessary steps, including appropriate formula substitutions, diagrams, graphs, charts, etc. Utilize the information provided for each question to determine your answer. Note that diagrams are not necessarily drawn to scale. For all questions in this part, a correct numerical answer with no work shown will receive only 1 credit. All answers should he written in pen, except for graphs and drawings, which should he done in pencil. [16]

33. Factor completely over the set of integers: $16x^4 - 81$. Sara graphed the polynomial $y = 16x^4 - 81$ and stated "All the roots of $y = 16x^4 - 81$ are real." Is Sara correct? Explain your reasoning.

   06 2019 33

34. The half-life of a radioactive substance is 15 years. Write an equation that can be used to determine the amount, $s(t)$, of 200 grams of this substance that remains after t years. Determine algebraically, to the *nearest year*, how long it will take for $\dfrac{1}{10}$ of this substance to remain.

   06 2019 34

35. Determine an equation for the parabola with focus $(4,-1)$ and directrix $y = -5$. (Use of the grid below is optional.)

06 2019 35

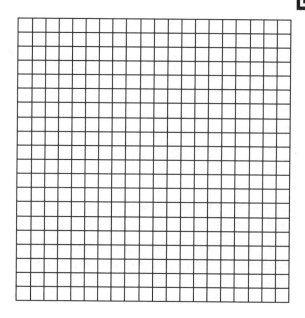

36. Juan and Filipe practice at the driving range before playing golf. The number of wins and corresponding practice times for each player are shown in the table below.

06 2019 36

	Juan Wins	Felipe Wins
Short Practice Time	8	10
Long Practice Time	15	12

Given that the practice time was long, determine the exact probability that Filipe wins the next match. Determine whether or not the two events "Filipe wins" and "long practice time" are independent. Justify your answer.

Part IV

Answer the question in this part. A correct answer will receive 6 credits. Clearly indicate the necessary steps, including appropriate formula substitutions, diagrams, graphs, charts, etc. Utilize the information provided to determine your answer. Note that diagrams are not necessarily drawn to scale. A correct numerical answer with no work shown will receive only 1 credit. All answers should be written in pen, except for graphs and drawings, which should be done in pencil. [6]

37. Griffin is riding his bike down the street in Churchville, N.Y. at a constant speed, when a nail gets caught in one of his tires. The height of the nail above the ground, in inches, can be represented by the trigonometric function

06 2019 37

$$f(t) = -13\cos(0.8\,\pi t) + 13,$$

where *t* represents the time (in seconds) since the nail first became caught in the tire. Determine the of $f(t)$. Interpret what the period represents in this context. On the grid below, graph *at least one* cycle of $f(t)$ that includes the *y*-intercept of the function.

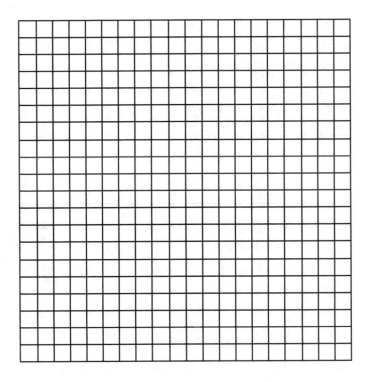

Does the height of the nail ever reach 30 inches above the ground? Justify your answer.

The University of the State of New York
REGENTS HIGH SCHOOL EXAMINATION

ALGEBRA II

Wednesday, August 14, 2019 - 12:30 to 3:30 p.m., only

Student Name _____

School Name _____

The possession or use of any communications device is strictly prohibited when taking this examination. If you have or use any communications device, no matter how briefly,
your examination will be invalidated and no score will be calculated for you.

Print your name and the name of your school on the lines above. A separate answer sheet for **Part I** has been provided to you. Follow the instructions from the proctor for completing the student information on your answer sheet.

This examination has four parts, with a total of 37 questions. You must answer all questions in this examination. Record your answers to the Part I multiple-choice questions on the separate answer sheet. Write your answers to the questions in **Parts II**, **III**, and **IV** directly in this booklet. All work
should be written in pen, except for graphs and drawings, which should be done in pencil. Clearly indicate the necessary steps, including appropriate formula substitutions, diagrams, graphs, charts, etc. Utilize the information provided for each question to determine your answer. Note that diagrams
are not necessarily drawn to scale. The formulas that you may need to answer some questions in this examination are found at the end of the examination. This sheet is perforated so you may remove it from this booklet. Scrap paper is not permitted for any part of this examination, but you may use the blank spaces in this booklet as scrap paper. A perforated sheet of scrap graph paper is provided at the end of this booklet for any question for which graphing may be helpful but is not required. You may remove this sheet from this booklet. Any work done on this sheet of scrap graph paper will not be scored. When you have completed the examination, you must sign the statement printed at the end of the answer sheet, indicating that you had no unlawful knowledge of the questions or answers prior to the examination and that you have neither given nor received assistance in answering any of
the questions during the examination. Your answer sheet cannot be accepted if you fail to sign this

Notice ...
A graphing calculator and a straightedge (ruler) must be available for you to use while taking this examination.

DO NOT OPEN THIS EXAMINATION BOOKLET UNTIL THE SIGNAL IS GIVEN.

Part I

Answer all 24 questions in this part. Each correct answer will receive 2 credits. No partial credit will be allowed. Utilize the information provided for each question to determine your answer. Note that diagrams are not necessarily drawn to scale. For each statement or question, choose the word or expression that, of those given, best completes the statement or answers the question. Record your answers on your separate answer sheet. [48]

1. When the expression $(x + 2)^2 + 4(x + 2) + 3$ is rewritten as the product of two binomials, the result is

    08 2019 01

    1) $(x + 3)(x + 1)$ 3) $(x + 2)(x + 2)$
    2) $(x + 5)(x + 3)$ 4) $(x + 6)(x + 1)$

2. The first term of a geometric sequence is 8 and the fourth term is 216. What is the sum of the first 12 terms of the corresponding series?

    08 2019 02

    1) 236,192   3) 2,125,760
    2) 708,584   4) 6,377,288

3. Perry invested in property that cost him $1500. Five years later it was worth $3000, and 10 years from his original purchase, it was worth $6000. Assuming the growth rate remains the same, which type of function could he create to find the value of his investment 30 years from his original purchase?

    08 2019 03

    1) exponential function   3) quadratic function
    2) linear function   4) trigonometric funct

4. If $\left(a^3 + 27\right) = (a + 3)\left(a^2 + ma + 9\right)$, then m equals

1) -9
3) 3
2) -3
4) 6

5. If $\cos \theta = -\dfrac{3}{4}$ and θ is in Quadrant III, then $\sin \theta$ is equivalent to

1) $-\dfrac{\sqrt{7}}{4}$
3) $-\dfrac{5}{4}$

2) $\dfrac{\sqrt{7}}{4}$
4) $\dfrac{5}{4}$

6. A veterinary pharmaceutical company plans to test a new drug to treat a common intestinal infection among puppies. The puppies are randomly assigned to two equal groups. Half of the puppies will receive the drug, and the other half will receive a placebo. The veterinarians monitor the puppies. This is an example of which study method?

1) census
3) survey
2) observational study
4) controlled experiment

7. The expression $2 - \dfrac{x-1}{x+2}$ is equivalent to

08 2019 07

1) $1 - \dfrac{3}{x+2}$

3) $1 - \dfrac{1}{x+2}$

2) $1 + \dfrac{3}{x+2}$

4) $1 + \dfrac{1}{x+2}$

8. Which description could represent the graph of $f(x) = 4x^2(x+a) - x - a$, if a is an integer?

08 2019 08

1) As $x \to -\infty$, $f(x) \to \infty$, as $x \to \infty$, $f(x) \to \infty$, and the graph has 3 x-intercepts.

3) As $x \to -\infty$, $f(x) \to \infty$, as $x \to \infty$, $f(x) \to -\infty$, and the graph has 4 x-intercepts.

2) As $x \to -\infty$, $f(x) \to -\infty$, as $x \to \infty$, $f(x) \to \infty$, and the graph has 3 x-intercepts.

4) As $x \to -\infty$, $f(x) \to -\infty$, as $x \to \infty$, $f(x) \to \infty$, and the graph has 4 x-intercepts.

9. After Roger's surgery, his doctor administered pain medication in the following amounts in milligrams over four days.

08 2019 09

Day (n)	1	2	3	4
Dosage (m)	2000	1680	1411.2	1185.4

How can this sequence best be modeled recursively?

1) $m_1 = 2000$
   $m_n = m_{n-1} - 320$

2) $m_n = 2000(0.84)^{n-1}$

3) $m_1 = 2000$
   $m_n = (0.84)m_{n-1}$

4) $m_n = 2000(0.84)^{n+1}$

10. The expression $\dfrac{9x^2 - 2}{3x + 1}$ is equivalent to

1) $3x - 1 - \dfrac{1}{3x+1}$

2) $3x - 1 + \dfrac{1}{3x+1}$

3) $3x + 1 - \dfrac{1}{3x+1}$

4) $3x + 1 + \dfrac{1}{3x+1}$

11. If $f(x)$ is an even function, which function must also be even?

1) $f(x-2)$

2) $f(x)+3$

3) $f(x+1)$

4) $f(x+1)+3$

12. The average monthly temperature of a city can be modeled by a cosine graph. Melissa has been living in Phoenix, Arizona, where the average annual temperature is 75°F. She would like to move, and live in a location where the average annual temperature is 62°F. When examining the graphs of the average monthly temperatures for various locations, Melissa should focus on the

08 2019 12

1) amplitude
2) horizontal shift

3) period
4) midline

13. Consider the probability statements regarding events A and B below.

$$P(A \text{ or } B) = 0.3;$$
$$P(A \text{ and } B) = 0.2; \text{ and}$$
$$P(A|B) = 0.8$$

What is $P(B)$?

1) 0.1   3) 0.375
2) 0.25   4) 0.667

14. Given $y > 0$, the expression $\sqrt{3x^2y} \cdot \sqrt[3]{27x^3y^2}$ is equivalent to

1) $81x^5y^3$ 3) $3^{\frac{5}{2}}x^2y^{\frac{5}{3}}$

2) $3^{15}x^2y$ 4) $3^{\frac{3}{2}}x^2y^{\frac{7}{6}}$

15. What is the solution set of the equation $\dfrac{10}{x^2 - 2x} + \dfrac{4}{x} = \dfrac{5}{x - 2}$?

1) $\{0, 2\}$ 3) $\{2\}$
2) $\{0\}$ 4) $\{\ \}$

16. What are the solution(s) to the system of equations shown below?

08 2019 16

$$x^2 + y^2 = 5$$

$$y = 2x$$

1) $x = 1$ and $x = -1$ 3) $(1, 2)$ and $(-1, -2)$
2) $x = 1$ 4) $(1, 2)$, only

17. If $5000 is put into a savings account that pays 3.5% interest compounded monthly, how much money, to the *nearest ten cents*, would be in that account after 6 years, assuming no money was added or withdrawn?

08 2019 17

1) $5177.80   3) $6146.30
2) $5941.30   4) $6166.50

18. The Fahrenheit temperature, $F(t)$, of a heated object at time t, in minutes, can be modeled by the function below. F_s is the surrounding temperature, F_0 is the initial temperature of the object, and k is a constant.

08 2019 18

$$F(t) = F_s + (F_0 - F_s)e^{-kt}$$

Coffee at a temperature of 195°F is poured into a container. The room temperature is kept at a constant 68°F and $k = 0.05$. Coffee is safe to drink when its temperature is, at most, 120°F. To the *nearest minute*, how long will it take until the coffee is safe to drink?

1) 7   3) 11
2) 10   4) 18

137

19. The mean intelligence quotient (IQ) score is 100, with a standard deviation of 15, and the scores are normally distributed. Given this information, the approximate percentage of the population with an IQ greater than 130 is closest to

    08 2019 19

    1) 2%   3) 48%
    2) 31%   4) 95%

20. After examining the functions
    $f(x) = \ln(x + 2)$ and $g(x) = e^{x-1}$
    over the interval $(-2, 3]$, Lexi determined that the correct number of solutions to the equation $f(x) = g(x)$ is

    08 2019 20

    1) 1   3) 3
    2) 2   4) 0

21. Evan graphed a cubic function,
    $f(x) = ax^3 + bx^2 + cx + d$, and determined the roots of $f(x)$ to be ± 1 and 2.
    What is the value of b, if $a = 1$?

    08 2019 21

    1) 1   3) −1
    2) 2   4) −2

22. The equation $t = \dfrac{1}{0.0105} \ln\left(\dfrac{A}{5000}\right)$ relates

    08 2019 22

    time, t, in years, to the amount of money, A, earned by a $5000 investment. Which statement accurately describes the relationship between the average rates of change of t on the intervals [6000, 8000] and [9000, 12,000]?

1) A comparison cannot be made because the intervals are different sizes.

2) The average rate of change is equal for both intervals.

3) The average rate of change is larger for the interval [6000, 8000].

4) The average rate of change is larger for the interval [9000, 12,000].

23. What is the inverse of $f(x) = \dfrac{x}{x+2}$, where $x \neq -2$?

08 2019 23

1) $f^{-1}(x) = \dfrac{2x}{x-1}$

3) $f^{-1}(x) = \dfrac{x}{x-2}$

2) $f^{-1}(x) = \dfrac{-2x}{x-1}$

4) $f^{-1}(x) = \dfrac{-x}{x-2}$

24. A study of black bears in the Adirondacks reveals that their population can be represented by the function $P(t) = 3500(1.025)^t$, where t is the number of years since the study began. Which function is correctly rewritten to reveal the monthly growth rate of the black bear population?

08 2019 24

1) $P(t) = 3500(1.00206)^{12t}$

3) $P(t) = 3500(1.34489)^{12t}$

2) $P(t) = 3500(1.00206)^{\frac{t}{12}}$

4) $P(t) = 3500(1.34489)^{\frac{t}{12}}$

Part II

Answer all 8 questions in this part. Each correct answer will receive 2 credits. Clearly indicate the necessary steps, including appropriate formula substitutions, diagrams, graphs, charts, etc. Utilize the information provided for each question to determine your answer. Note that diagrams are not necessarily drawn to scale. For all questions in this part, a correct numerical answer with no work shown will receive only I credit. All answers should be written in pen, except for graphs and drawings, which should be done in pencil. [16]

25. At Andrew Jackson High School, students are only allowed to enroll in AP U.S. History if they have already taken AP World History or AP European History.
Out of 825 incoming seniors, 165 took AP History, 66 took AP European History, and 33 took both. Given this information, determine the probability a randomly selected incoming senior is allowed to enroll in AP U.S. History.

08 2019 25

26. Explain what a rational exponent, such as $\frac{5}{2}$ means. Use this explanation to evaluate $9^{\frac{5}{2}}$.

08 2019 26

27. Write $-\frac{1}{2}i^3\left(\sqrt{-9}-4\right)-3i^2$ in simplest $a+bi$ form.

08 2019 27

140

28. A person's lung capacity can be modeled by the function $C(t) = 250 \sin\left(\dfrac{2\pi}{5} t\right) + 2450$, where $C(t)$ represents the volume in mL present in the lungs after t seconds. State the maximum value of this function over one full cycle, and explain what this value represents.

29. Determine for which polynomial(s) $(x + 2)$ is a factor. Explain your answer.

$$P(x) = x^4 - 3x^3 - 16x - 12$$
$$Q(x) = x^3 - 3x^2 - 16x - 12$$

30. On July 21, 2016, the water level in Puget Sound, WA reached a high of 10.1 ft at 6 a.m. and a low of -2 ft at 12:30 p.m. Across the country in Long Island, NY, Shinnecock Bay's water level reached a high of 2.5 ft at 10:42 p.m. and a low of -0.1 ft at 5:31 a.m. The water levels of both locations are affected by the tides and can be modeled by sinusoidal functions. Determine the difference in amplitudes, in feet, for these two locations.

31.   Write a recursive formula, a_n,
       to describe the sequence graphed below.

08 2019 31

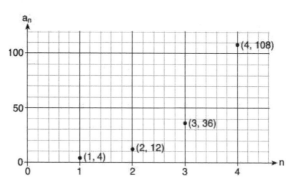

32.   Sketch the graphs of
       $r(x) = \dfrac{1}{x}$ and $a(x) = |x| - 3$
       on the set of axes below.

       Determine, to the *nearest tenth*,
       the positive solution of $r(x) = a(x)$.

08 2019 32

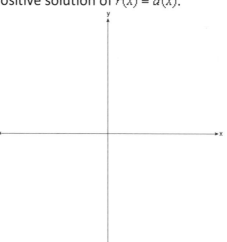

Part III

Answer all 4 questions in this part. Each correct answer will receive 4 credits. Clearly indicate the necessary steps, including appropriate formula substitutions, diagrams, graphs, charts, etc. Utilize the information provided for each question to determine your answer. Note that diagrams are not necessarily drawn to scale. For all questions in this part, a correct numerical answer with no work shown will receive only 1 credit. All answers should he written in pen, except for graphs and drawings, which should he done in pencil. [16]

33.   A population of 950 bacteria grows continuously at a rate of 4.75% per day. Write an exponential function, $N(t)$, that represents the bacterial population after t days and explain the reason for your choice of base. Determine the bacterial population after 36 hours, to the *nearest bacterium*.

08 2019 33

34. Write an equation for a sine function with an amplitude of 2 and a period of $\frac{\pi}{2}$.

On the grid below, sketch the graph of the equation in the interval 0 to 2π.

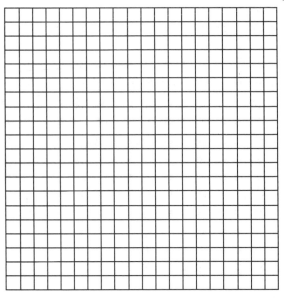

35. Mary bought a pack of candy. The manufacturer claims that 30% of the candies manufactured are red. In her pack, 14 of the 60 candies are red. She ran a simulation of 300 samples, assuming the manufacturer is correct. The results are shown below.

08 2019 35

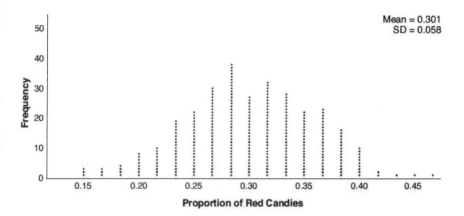

Based on the simulation, determine the middle 95% of plausible values that the proportion of red candies in a pack is within. Based on the simulation, is it unusual that Mary's pack had 14 red candies out of a total of 60? Explain.

36.   a) Algebraically determine the roots, $\;\;\;\;$ 08 2019 36
in simplest $a + bi$ form, to the equation
below.

$$x^2 - 2x + 7 = 4x - 10$$

b) Consider the system of equations below.
$$y = x^2 - 2x + 7$$
$$y = 4x - 10$$
The graph of this system confirms the solution
from part a is imaginary. Explain why.

John correctly rounded the difference of the means of his
experimental groups as 7. How did John obtain this value
and what does it represent in the given context? Justify
your answer. To determine if there is any significance in this
value, John rerandomized the 16 scores into two groups of
8, calculated the difference of the means, and simulated this
process 250 times as shown below.

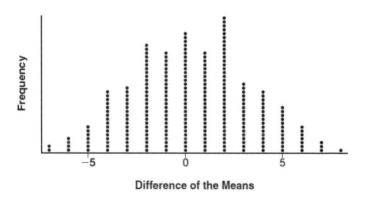

Classical vs. Rap

Difference of the Means

Does the simulation support the theory that there may be a
significant difference in quiz scores? Explain.

Part IV

Answer the question in this part. A correct answer will receive 6 credits. Clearly indicate the necessary steps, including appropriate formula substitutions, diagrams, graphs, charts, etc. Utilize the information provided to determine your answer. Note that diagrams are not necessarily drawn to scale. A correct numerical answer with no work shown will receive only 1 credit. All answers should be written in pen, except for graphs and drawings, which should be done in pencil. [6]

37.   The Beaufort Wind Scale was devised by British Rear Admiral Sir Francis Beaufort, in 1805 based upon observations of the effects of the wind. Beaufort numbers, B, are determined by the equation

08 2019 37

$$B = 1.69\sqrt{s + 4.45} - 3.49,$$

where *s* is the speed of the wind in mph, and *B* is rounded to the nearest integer from 0 to 12.

Beaufort Wind Scale	
Beaufort Number	**Force of Wind**
0	Calm
1	Light air
2	Light breeze
3	Gentle breeze
4	Moderate breeze
5	Fresh breeze
6	Steady breeze
7	Moderate gale
8	Fresh gale
9	Strong gale
10	Whole gale
11	Storm
12	Hurricane

Using the table above, classify the force of wind at a speed of 30 mph. Justify your answer. In 1946, the scale was extended to accommodate strong hurricanes. A strong hurricane received a *B* value of exactly 15. Algebraically determine the value of *s*, to the *nearest mph*. Any *B* values that round to 10 receive a Beaufort number of 10. Using technology, find an approximate range of wind speeds, to the *nearest mph*, associated with a Beaufort number of 10

Accepted Solutions and Point Allocation

Polynomial Expressions and Equations

1. [4] 0, a correct explanation is written, $-4, \frac{3}{2}, 4$ and correct algebraic work is shown.

2. [2] $(x^2 - 6)(x^2 + 2)$

3. [2] 4

4. [2] 3

5. [2] 3

6. [2] 1

7. [2] 4

8. [2] $2a^2 + 5a + 2 - \frac{5}{3a-2}$, or an equivalent answer, and correct algebraic work is shown.

9. [2] 4

10. [2] 4

11. [2] 1

12. [2] 3

13. [2] 1

14. [2] 2

15. [2] A positive cubic function is sketched and with its roots at $-c$, b, then a, and a y-intercept at d.

16. [2] A correct verification is written.

17. [2] 2

18. [2] 1

19. [2] 1

20. [2] 4

21. [2] 4

22. [2] 2

Accepted Solutions and Point Allocation

23. [2] $(x^2 + 4)(4x - 1)$ and correct work is shown.
24. [2] -6, and a correct explanation is written.
25. [2] 4
26. [2] 3
27. [2] 4
28. [2] 1
29. [2] 2
30. [2] 3
31. [2] 2
32. [2] 3
33. [2] 4
34. [2] 3
35. [4] -1, $+/-2$, and correct algebraic work is shown and $P(x)$ is graphed correctly.
36. [2] 1
37. [2] 1
38. [2] 4
39. [2] No, and correct work is shown, and a correct explanation is written.
40. [2] (4,0), and correct work is shown.
41. [4] g, and a correct justification is given.

Accepted Solutions and Point Allocation

Complex Numbers

1. [2] 4
2. [2] 3
3. [2] $-\frac{5}{4} \pm \frac{\sqrt{39}}{4} i$ or equivalent $a + bi$ form, and
    correct work is shown.
4. [2] 3
5. [2] 3
6. [2] 3
7. [2] 4
8. [2] 2
9. [2] 4
10. [2] $-36xi$, and correct work is shown.
11. [2] 2

Exponential Expressions and Equations

1. [4] 18.5, and correct work is shown.
2. [2] 48.78, and correct work is shown.
3. [2] $\sqrt{x}$ and correct work is shown.
4. [2] 1
5. [2] 4 ⸺
6. [2] 2
7. [2] 4
8. [4] $C(t) = 63,000 \left(1 + \frac{0.0255}{12}\right)^{12t}$ or
    equivalent, 18.14 and correct algebraic
    work shown.
9. [2] $624, and correct work is shown.
10. [2] 4

11. [2] 4
12. [2] 1
13. [2] 1
14. [2] 1
15. [2] 2
16. [2] 2
17. [6] Correct graphs are drawn and at least one is labeled, 1.95 and a correct explanation, and 6 and a correct justification is given.
18. [4] $y = 4.168(3.981)^x$ and 2 hours 15 minutes or an equivalent time, and correct work is shown.
19. [2] 4, and correct algebraic work is shown.
20. [2] 3
21. [2] 3
22. [6] $100 = 140\left(\frac{1}{2}\right)^{\frac{5}{h}}$ or equivalent, 10.3002, 18.6, and correct work is shown.
23. [4] 1247 and 20,407, and correct work is shown.
24. [2] $x^{\frac{5}{6}}$ and correct work is shown.
25. [2] 2
26. [2] 2
27. [2] 4
28. [2] 3
29. [2] 1
30. [2] 1
31. [2] 4
32. [2] 4
33. [4] 12, and correct work is shown.

Accepted Solutions and Point Allocation

34. [6] Correct functions are written, such as $A = 5000(1.045)^n$, $B = 5000(1.0115)^{4n}$ and 67.57, 15.2, and correct work is shown.

35. [2] 4

36. [2] 4

37. [2] 3

38. [2] 6, and correct work is shown.

39. [4] $S_n = \dfrac{33{,}000 - 33{,}000(1.04)^n}{1 - 1.04}$ or an equivalent equation is written and 660,778.39, and correct work is shown.

40. [6] $A(t) = 800e^{-0.347t}$ and $B(t) = 400e^{-0.231t}$, correct graphs are drawn and at least one is labeled, 6, 5.5, and correct work is shown.

Rational Expressions and Equations

1. [2] 0, 3 and correct algebraic work is shown.

2. [2] 3

3. [2] 4

4. [4] −5, −1 and correct work is shown.

5. [2] 1

6. [2] 3

7. [2] 2

8. [2] 4, and correct work is shown.

9. [2] A correct algebraic proof is shown.

Accepted Solutions and Point Allocation

Radical Expressions and Equations

1.   [2] 3
2.   [2] 3
3.   [4] −15, and correct algebraic work is shown.
4.   [2] 2
5.   [2] 3
6.   [2] A correct explanation is written.
7.   [2] 4
8.   [2] 2
9.   [2] 5 and correct algebraic work is shown.
10.   [2] A correct explanation is written.
11.   [4] 4, correct algebraic work is shown, and a correct justification and rejection are given.
12.   [2] 3

Accepted Solutions and Point Allocation

Trigonometric Expressions and Equations

1.   [2] 2
2.   [2] 2
3.   [4] −12 and correct work is shown, 2.2, 3.8, and a correct justification is given.
4.   [2] $\frac{-1}{\sqrt{5}}$, or an equivalent answer and work is shown.
5.   [2] 4
6.   [4] A correct sketch with at least one cycle is drawn and a correct explanation is written.
7.   [2] 4
8.   [2] 4
9.   [2] 3
10.   [2] 2/3 and a correct description is written.
11.   [2] 4
12.   [2] 2
13.   [2] 1
14.   [2] 4
15.   [2] 2
16.   [2] 1
17.   [2] Amplitude, and a correct explanation is given.
18.   [2] −1.02, and correct work using the identity is shown.
19.   [2] 3
20.   [2] 1
21.   [2] 4
22.   [2] A correct graph is drawn.

Accepted Solutions and Point Allocation

Graphing

1. [6] $P(x) = -330x^3 + 9000x^2 - 67,000x + 167,000$, a correct graph is drawn over $2 \leq x \leq 16$, 5 and 13, and a correct explanation is written.
2. [2] A correct graph on $[0, 2\pi]$ is drawn.
3. [2] 4
4. [2] 1
5. [2] 4
6. [2] 2
7. [6] 1.1, correct graphs, 14,000 visits, and correct work is shown.
8. [2] A correct graph is drawn.
9. [2] 2
10. [4] A correct graph is drawn and a correct description is given, such as $x \to -3$, $y \to -\infty$, and as $x \to \infty$, $y \to \infty$.
11. [2] A correct graph is drawn.
12. [2] 2
13. [2] 1
14. [2] 2
15. [2] 3
16. [2] 4
17. [2] 3
18. [2] 1
19. [2] 2

Accepted Solutions and Point Allocation

Functions

1. [2] 3
2. [2] 2
3. [2] 3
4. [2] 2
5. [2] Even, and correct algebraic work is shown.
6. [2] 2
7. [2] 1
8. [2] 3
9. [2] 1
10. [2] f, and a correct justification is given.
11. [2] 7.5, and a correct explanation is written.
12. [2] 4
13. [2] 2
14. [2] 4

Accepted Solutions and Point Allocation

Systems of Equations

1. [4] $x = -2$, $y = 5$, $z = 3$, and correct algebraic work is shown.
2. [2] (12, −16), (16, −12) and correct algebraic work is shown.
3. [2] 1
4. [4] $x = 0$, $y = 2$, and $z = -1$, and correct algebraic work is shown.
5. [2] 2
6. [4] (7, −2) and (3, 2) or equivalent solutions, and correct algebraic work is shown.

Sequences and Series

1. [2] 3, 7, 15, 31, No, and a correct justification is given.
2. [4] $a_n = 1.25 + 0.25(n - 1)$ or an equivalent equation, and 16, and correct work is shown.
3. [2] A correct recursive formula, such as
$$a_1 = 4$$
$$a_n = 2a_{n-1} + 1,$$
639, and correct work is shown.
4. [2] 3
5. [2] 4
6. [2] 3
7. [2] 1
8. [2] 1
9. [2] 3
10. [2] 4
11. [2] 3

Accepted Solutions and Point Allocation

Probability

1.   [2] 4
2.   [2] 2
3.   [2] $\dfrac{103}{213}$
4.   [2] 4
5.   [2] 0.8 or an equivalent value, and correct work is shown.
6.   [2] Both siblings jog and a correct justification is given.
7.   [2] 2
8.   [2] 1
9.   [2] Independent, and correct work is shown.
10.   [2] 1
11.   [2] $\dfrac{108}{1376}$ or an equivalent fraction, and correct work is shown.

Statistics

1.   [4] A correct justification, yes, and a correct explanation is given.
2.   [2] A correct margin of error is written, such as 0.08, and a correct explanation is written.
3.   [2] 941, and correct work is shown.
4.   [2] 2
5.   [4] 5, a correct interval is stated such as (−3.07, 3.13), and correct work is shown, yes and a correct explanation is written.
6.   [2] A correct statistical bias is explained.
7.   [2] 2

Accepted Solutions and Point Allocation

8. [2] A correct explanation is written, such as assigning a flavor to a number and observing the number of times 4 of the same flavor occurred consecutively.

9. [2] 1

10. [2] 2

11. [2] 2

12. [2] 1

13. [4] A correct interval is stated, such as (0.35, 0.66), and correct work is shown, and a correct explanation is written.

14. [2] 69, and correct work is shown.

15. [2] 3

16. [2] 3

17. [2] 1

18. [2] 3

19. [2] 2

20. [2] Yes, and a correct justification is given, and correct work is shown.

21. [4] Both explanations are correctly written.

22. [2] 3

23. [2] 3

24. [2] 2

25. [2] A correct description of a controlled experiment is written, such as indicating two randomly assigned groups, one with ingredient X and one without ingredient X.

26. [4] (0.47, 0.73) and correct work is shown, and a correct statistical explanation is written.

The University of the State of New York
REGENTS HIGH SCHOOL EXAMINATION
ALGEBRA II
Friday, June 21, 2019 - 1:15 to 4:15 p.m., only
Part I

Allow a total of 48 credits, 2 credits for each of the following.

(1). . . . . 3 . . . . .   (2). . . . . 4 . . . . .   (3). . . . . 3 . . . . .

(4). . . . . 1 . . . . .   (5). . . . . 4 . . . . .   (6). . . . . 3 . . . . .

(7). . . . . 4 . . . . .   (8). . . . . 1 . . . . .   (9). . . . . 2 . . . . .

(10). . . . 3 . . . . .   (11) . . . . 2 . . . .   (12) . . . .4 . . . .

(13). . . . 2 . . . . .   (14) . . . . 4 . . . .   (15) . . . . 1 . . . .

(16). . . . 1 . . . . .   (17) . . . . 2 . . . .   (18) . . . . 4 . . . .

(19) . . . . 2 . . . .   (20) . . . . 1 . . . .   (21) . . . . 4 . . . .

(22).. . . . 3 . . . .   (23) . . . . 2 . . . .   (24) . . . . 4 . . . .

Part II

For each question, use the specific criteria to award a maximum of 2 credits. Unless otherwise specified, mathematically correct alternative solutions should be awarded appropriate credit.

(25) [2] 1.5, and a correct interpretation is written.

(26) [2] $\{-2,7\}$, and correct algebraic work is shown.

(27) [2] A correct graph is drawn.

(28) [2] $-\frac{24}{25}$ or equivalent, and correct work is shown.

(29) [2] A correct justification indicating a negative response is given. No.
$$\left(\sqrt[7]{x^2}\right)\left(\sqrt[5]{x^3}\right) = x^{\frac{2}{7}} \; x^{\frac{3}{5}} = x^{\frac{31}{35}}\left(\sqrt[35]{x^{31}}\right)$$

(30) [2] $x^3 - x^2 + 7x - 2$ is stated and correct work is shown.

(31) [2] $a_1 = 6$
$a_n = \frac{3}{2}a_{n-1}$ or equivalent is written.

(32) [2] No or not unfair, and a correct explanation is written. No.
$0.499 \pm 2(0.049) \rightarrow 0.401 - 0.597$.
Since 0.43 falls within this interval, Robin's coin is likely not unfair.

Part III

For each question, use the specific criteria to award a maximum of 4 credits. Unless otherwise specified, mathematically correct alternative solutions should be awarded appropriate credit.

(33) [4] $(4x^2 + 9)(2x + 3)(2x - 3)$, and correct work is shown, and a correct explanation indicating a negative response is written.

(34) [4] $s(t) = 200 \left(\frac{1}{2}\right)^{\frac{t}{15}}$ or equivalent, 50 and correct algebraic work is shown.

(35) [4] $y + 3 = \frac{1}{8}(x - 4)^2$, or an equivalent equation, and correct work is shown.

(36) [4] $\frac{12}{27}$ or equivalent and correct work is shown, not independent and a correct justification is given.

Part IV

For each question, use the specific criteria to award a maximum of 6 credits. Unless otherwise specified, mathematically correct alternative solutions should be awarded appropriate credit.

(37) [6] 2.5, a correct interpretation is written, a correct graph is drawn, and a correct justification indicating a negative response is given.

Answers - August 2019 Algebra II Regents Exam

The University of the State of New York
REGENTS HIGH SCHOOL EXAMINATION
ALGEBRA II

Wednesday, August 14, 2019 - 12:30 to 3:30 p.m., only

Part I

Allow a total of 48 credits, 2 credits for each of the following.

(1) . . . . . 2 . . . . .   (2) . . . . 3 . . . . .   (3) . . . . . 1 . . . . .

(4) . . . . . 2 . . . . .   (5) . . . . . 1 . . . . .   (6) . . . . . 4 . . . . .

(7) . . . . 2 . . . . .   (8) . . . . . 2 . . . . .   (9) . . . . 3 . . . . .

(10) . . . . 1 . . . . . .   (11) . . . . .2 . . . . .   (12). . . . .4 . . . . .

(13) . . . . 2 . . . . .   (14) .. . . . 4 . . . . .   (15). . . . .4 . . . . .

(16) . . . .3 . . . . .   (17) .. . . . 4 . . . . .   (18). . . . .4 . . . . .

(19) . . . . 1 . . . . .   (20) .. . . . 2 . . . . .   (21) . . . .4 . . . . .

(22) . . . .3 . . . . .   (23) .. . . . 2 . . . . .   (24) . . . . 1 . . . . .

Answers - August 2019 Algebra II Regents Exam

Part II

For each question, use the specific criteria to award a maximum of 2 credits. Unless otherwise specified, mathematically correct alternative solutions should be awarded appropriate credit.

(25) [2] 0.24 or equivalent and correct work is shown.

(26) [2] A correct explanation is written, such as 2 is the root and 5 is the power, and 243.

(27) [2] $\frac{3}{2} - 2i$, and correct work is shown.

(28) [2] 2700, and a correct explanation is written, such as the number of mL when the lungs are full.

29) [2] $Q(x)$, and correct work is shown, and a correct explanation is written.

(30) [2] 4.75 or –4.75, and correct work is shown.

(31) [2] A correct recursive formula is written, such as $a_1 = 4 \; and \; a_n = 3a_{n-1}$.

(32) [2] Correct sketches are drawn and 3.3.

Answers - August 2019 Algebra II Regents Exam

Part III

For each question, use the specific criteria to award a maximum of 4 credits. Unless otherwise specified, mathematically correct alternative solutions should be awarded appropriate credit.

(33) [4] $N(t) = 950e^{0.0475t}$, a correct explanation is written, 1020 and correct work is shown.

(34) [4] A correct equation, such as $y = 2 \sin 4x$, and a correct sketch is drawn.

(35) [4] A correct interval is determined, such as (0.185, 0.417) or equivalent notation, No is indicated, and a correct explanation is written.

(36) [4] $3 \pm \left(2\sqrt{2}\right)i$ or $3 \pm 2i\sqrt{2}$ and correct algebraic work is shown, and a correct explanation is written.

Part IV

For each question, use the specific criteria to award a maximum of 6 credits. Unless otherwise specified, mathematically correct alternative solutions should be awarded appropriate credit.

(37)   [6] Steady breeze and a correct justification is given, 115 and correct work is shown, and 55-64 is stated.

NOTES

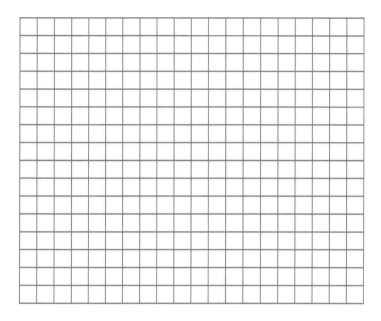

NOTES:

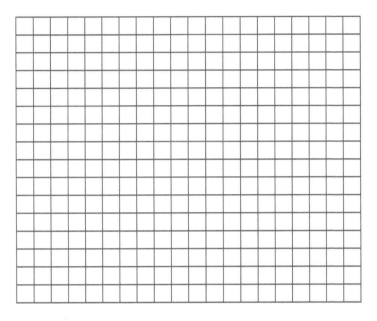

NOTES:

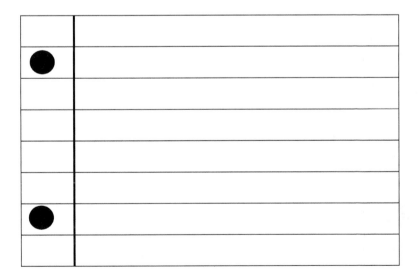

NOTES

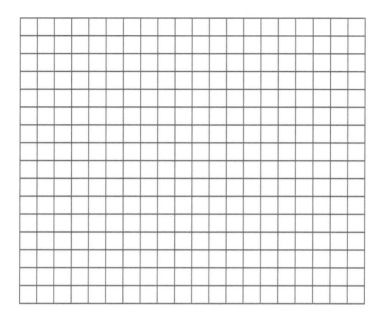

NOTES:

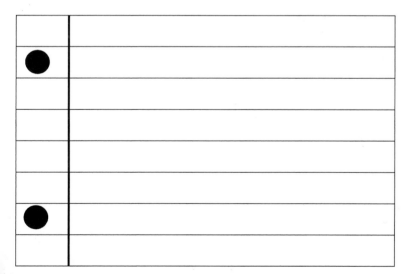

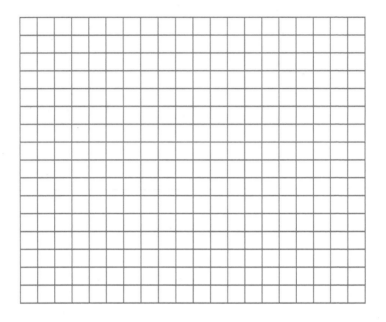

NOTES:

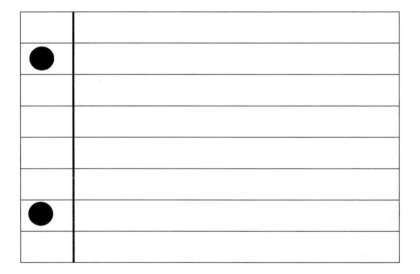